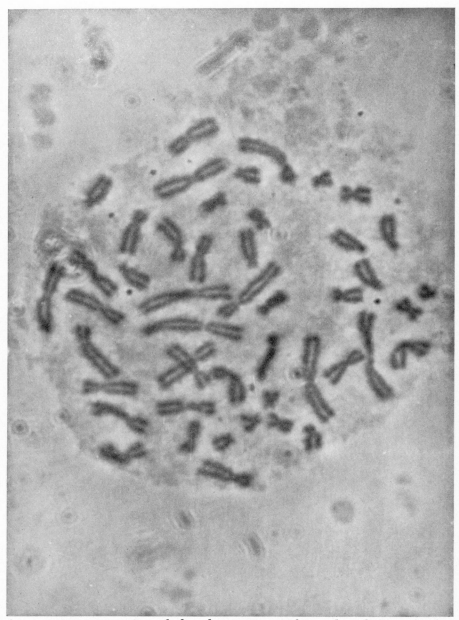

An average preparation of the chromosomes of a girl with Down's syndrome. Much better preparations and photographs can be made. Anyone can count the chromosomes shown and confirm that there are 47 of them. The preparation and photograph were made by my graduate student, Robert Goodlin, M.D.

SECOND EDITION

SHELDON C. REED, Ph.D.

DIRECTOR, DIGHT INSTITUTE FOR HUMAN
GENETICS, THE UNIVERSITY OF MINNESOTA

COUNSELING IN MEDICAL GENETICS

W. B. SAUNDERS COMPANY

PHILADELPHIA AND LONDON   1963

PREFACE TO THE

SECOND EDITION

The first edition of this book was written primarily to organize my thoughts and experiences in the field of genetic counseling. It was hoped that physicians would read it in order to give them a feeling for the subject. Most physicians are asked about heredity, but few find these questions sufficiently vexing to demand serious study of the subject of medical genetics. It was my hope that if the book were kept short enough and written in a light enough vein, a reasonable proportion of the medical profession might read it, and thus be introduced to a most important and exciting discipline. It was, like my first child, an experimental model. The book was read by many thousands of physicians, and most, as far as I can tell, still remember Professor Hooton's description of the ectomorph but not so many retain all of my simple genetics.

In this new version, I will try to make the genetics more understandable. The justification for a new edition is that medical genetics has had a phenomenal development during the last

v

few years. It has been necessary to completely rewrite the book because of the recent advances in our knowledge. Little of the old information has fallen away but much that is new has been added. Consequently, the new edition must be longer. The wealth of counseling experiences is now greater; over 2500 "cases" have been handled at the Dight Institute, the majority of them by the writer. In no case has there been any evidence of ill feeling toward the counselor, and the spontaneous gratitude of many of those who have been helped has been one of the finest experiences of my life.

It is my hope that this book will give the physician a better background with which to answer the questions in human genetics which pop up at the most unexpected times. Medical genetics should not be approached as if it were a morbid subject full of threats to everyone but as a new science with hope for all. It was so much fun writing this book, even though for the second time, that some of the pleasure ought to rub off onto the reader. I hope it will!

SHELDON C. REED

CONTENTS

Chapter 1

"In the Beginning" 1

Chapter 2

What Are the Problems? 6

Chapter 3

A Philosophy for Counseling 10

Chapter 4

A Few Laws 16

Chapter 5

Twins 22

Chapter 6

The Ubiquitous Heterozygote (or, The Common
Carrier) 28

Chapter 7

       DON'T MARRY A RELATIVE! 34

Chapter 8

       THE CHROMOSOME BREAK-THROUGH 42

Chapter 9

       DOWN'S SYNDROME (MONGOLISM) 49

Chapter 10

       MENTAL RETARDATION 59

Chapter 11

       THE CENTRAL NERVOUS SYSTEM SYNDROME 72

Chapter 12

       "CURES" FOR GENETIC DISEASES (PHENYLKETONURIA, FIBROCYSTIC DISEASE AND DIABETES) 83

Chapter 13

       MORE "CURES" FOR GENETIC DISEASES (PYLORIC STENOSIS AND CONGENITAL DISLOCATION OF THE HIP) .. 97

Chapter 14

       STILL MORE "CURES" FOR GENETIC DISEASES (RHEUMATIC FEVER AND TUBERCULOSIS) 109

Chapter 15

       HARELIP AND CLEFT PALATE (OF MICE AND MEN) .. 118

Chapter 16

       CLUBFOOT 126

Contents

Chapter 17

ALLERGIES 132

Chapter 18

BLOOD GENETICS 137

Chapter 19

DISPUTED PATERNITY 147

Chapter 20

SKIN COLOR 155

Chapter 21

STRING BEANS AND CHUBBIES 163

Chapter 22

HEART DISEASES 172

Chapter 23

CANCERS 178

Chapter 24

CONVULSIVE SEIZURES 183

Chapter 25

THE SCHIZOPHRENIAS 194

Chapter 26

MANIC-DEPRESSIVE PSYCHOSIS 205

Chapter 27

GENETIC EFFECTS OF RADIATIONS 212

Chapter 28

THE ENVIRONMENT 218

Chapter 29

PUTTING THE PUZZLE TOGETHER 225

APPENDIX: THE RARE GENETIC TRAITS 232

GENERAL LITERATURE CITED 259

INDEX 271

Chapter 1

"IN THE BEGINNING"

The Bible starts with the above three words and proceeds to describe the creation of the world and the evolution of plant and animal life, including man, in the first six paragraphs. Such brevity can hardly be equaled, but an attempt will be made to outline the development of human genetics and heredity clinics in as few words as possible.

The fact of heredity was clearly stated in various books of the Bible, and the concept that both the good and bad characteristics of an individual are in large part a biologic legacy from his ancestors was perhaps accepted more explicitly then than it is now. But the rules by which heredity works were not known in the beginning; they were first demonstrated by an Austrian monk, Gregor Mendel. It was not until our own century that the significance of the mendelian rules was appreciated. One of the first to see the applications of the mendelian rules to the welfare of man was Dr. C. B. Davenport, who established the Eugenics Record Office at Cold Spring Harbor, New York, in 1910.

On March 1, 1927, Charles F. Dight, M.D., wrote his bequest providing funds for the eventual founding of a counseling center at the University of Minnesota. Since Dr. Dight was exceedingly sound in mind and body, it was not until 1941 that the Dight Institute was opened, with Dr. C. P. Oliver as

TABLE 1   Location, Name of Institution and Principal Counselor of Twenty-eight Genetics Centers

Location	Institution	Counselor
Berkeley, California	University of California	Dr. Curt Stern
Los Angeles, California	Los Angeles Medical Center	Dr. Stanley Wright
Seattle, Washington	Department of Medicine University of Washington	Dr. Arno Motulsky
Edmonton, Alberta	Heredity Counseling Service University of Alberta	Dr. Margaret W. Thompson
Tempe, Arizona	Arizona State University	Dr. C. M. Woolf
Austin, Texas	The Genetics Foundation University of Texas	Dr. C. P. Oliver
Norman, Oklahoma	Department of Zoological Sciences University of Oklahoma	Dr. P. R. David
Winnipeg, Manitoba	Hospital for Sick Children	Dr. Irene Uchida
Minneapolis, Minnesota	University of Minnesota	Dr. S. C. Reed
Minneapolis, Minnesota	Human Genetics Unit State Board of Health	Dr. L. E. Schacht
Rochester, Minnesota	Mayo Clinic	Dr. J. S. Pearson
New Orleans, Louisiana	Genetic Counseling Service Tulane University	Dr. H. W. Kloepfer
Madison, Wisconsin	Department of Medical Genetics University of Wisconsin	Dr. J. F. Crow
Chicago, Illinois	Children's Memorial Hospital	Dr. David Y-Y. Hsia
Ann Arbor, Michigan	The Heredity Clinic University of Michigan	Dr. J. V. Neel
East Lansing, Michigan	Department of Zoology Michigan State University	Dr. J. V. Higgins
Cleveland, Ohio	Department of Biology Western Reserve University	Dr. A. G. Steinberg
Winston-Salem, North Carolina	Bowman Gray School of Medicine	Dr. C. N. Herndon
Toronto, Canada	Hospital for Sick Children	Dr. N. F. Walker
Charlottesville, Virginia	School of Medicine University of Virginia	Dr. R. F. Shaw
Washington, D. C.	Genetics Counseling Research Center George Washington University Hospital	Dr. N. C. Myrianthopoulos
Baltimore, Maryland	Johns Hopkins Hospital	Dr. V. A. McKusick
New York, New York	Albert Einstein College of Medicine Yeshiva University	Dr. S. G. Waelsch Dr. Helen Ranney
New York, New York	New York State Psychiatric Institute	Dr. F. J. Kallmann
New York, New Rock	Rockefeller Institute	Dr. A. G. Bearn
Montreal, Quebec	Children's Memorial Hospital	Dr. F. C. Fraser
Providence, Rhode Island	Department of Biology Brown University	Dr. G. W. Hagy
Boston, Massachusetts	Department of Immunochemistry Boston University Medical School	Dr. W. C. Boyd

director. Meanwhile, in 1940, the Heredity Clinic of the University of Michigan was initiated through the efforts of Dr. L. R. Dice. Several geneticists had given counseling for many years before 1941, but only since then have heredity clinics been recognized as useful institutions in the community. There are now more than 20 places that function as heredity clinics, and all give counseling and information free of charge. Some of these are listed in Table I, where they are arranged geographically from west to east. If any one of these persons is unable to help you, he or she will refer you to another center.

The policy of the heredity clinics of giving free consultation means that their financial condition is likely to be unstable. Most of them survive only because of the broad-minded generosity of various public and private agencies. Support for the Dight Institute, in addition to its original endowment, has come from generous gifts from the Rockefeller Foundation. The purpose of the Rockefeller grants was to support the counseling program as a research problem, with the expectation that the potentialities of heredity clinics would be determined. The reader can judge from the case reports in subsequent chapters whether genetic counseling is a public necessity or merely a luxury.

The reader may appreciate a quick introduction to Dr. C. F. Dight, whose bequest established the heredity clinic at Minnesota and ensures its continuity, even though the major support for the counseling program must be obtained elsewhere.

Dr. Dight had many idiosyncrasies. For some years he lived in a house that he had built in a tree. It was on stilts and was entered by means of a spiral iron stairway. There were appropriate proverbs painted over the doors, such as "Truth Shall Triumph, Justice Shall be Law." He was the medical examiner for a small insurance company but did not bother with private practice. His money accumulated as a result of exag-

gerated frugality, shrewd investments and a calculated failure
to file income tax returns. He always had a petition in his pocket.

Unusual people like Dr. Dight often contribute invaluable
gifts to society. Dr. Dight was primarily responsible for the
adoption of a Minneapolis city ordinance enforcing milk pas-
teurization. Forty years ago this was considered a radical attack
on the rights of the milk companies, but it prevented many
cases of undulant fever and other milk-borne diseases. He fought
for and obtained an efficient garbage removal service and insti-
gated the foundation of a public market. But his greatest interest
centered in the application of Mendel's laws of heredity to the
welfare of mankind.

Dr. Dight built his house in a tree because he was afraid
of grass fires; but he was not afraid to fight for the use of science
and intelligence in the improvement of our social and biologic
inheritance. He realized that practically every family had problems resulting from their particular heredity and that many of
the problems could be solved if there were a center where the
family could get the facts about human genetics. The idea became a fact, and well over 2,500 families or individuals have
received education and consequent understanding of problems
due to their heredity at the Dight Institute for Human Genetics
of the University of Minnesota. Heredity clinics have popped
up like mushrooms during the last decade, and what was once
just an idea should soon be a significant practical part of our
culture and a potent weapon in the fight against disease.

The first legal recognition that Dr. Dight was right came
in 1959, when the legislature of the State of Minnesota passed
an act authorizing the State Board of Health to conduct a Program for Study of Human Genetics Problems. A unit for human
genetics was established promptly in the Division for Special
Services of the State Board of Health. It provides genetic counseling and general education in medical genetics. Both the Dight

Institute and the State Board of Health unit are encouraged and strengthened by a group of interested laymen known as the Minnesota Human Genetics League. This vigorous organization was formed according to the terms of Dr. Dight's bequest. It is remarkable that as a result of this small bequest of money, accompanied by appropriate directions, Minnesota became the first state officially to establish a unit for human genetics in its public health program.

Counseling in medical genetics is a most important practical application of the findings of the science of human genetics. It could help almost every family if available to them. We are still in the beginning stages of the development of sound practices in genetic counseling. As long as we do not take ourselves too seriously but instead approach the problems in a light-hearted manner, there will be no danger of the gory excesses committed in the name of eugenics in the past.

Chapter 2

WHAT ARE THE
PROBLEMS?

Counseling in human genetics is highly stimulating because of the incredible variety of the problems. A representative of the Roman Catholic Church inquires as to the probability that a lad with a family history of epilepsy will develop the disease. If the chance is great, the Church would not accept him for training for the priesthood. A welfare agency wants to know whether a child that is to be born to a brother-sister union is likely to be normal, and whether or not the child should be placed for adoption. A couple have had an albino baby and wish to know what chance there is of a repetition of this misfortune. A young woman wants to know what chance she has of developing Huntington's chorea, the disease which changed her father from a stalwart man-mountain into a demented shaking mass of protoplasm. An obstetrician has delivered two babies with spina bifida for one patient. He would like to make sure that this unpleasant situation won't occur again at the conclusion of his patient's third pregnancy. A physician and his wife have a baby boy with harelip and cleft palate. They had never thought that this would happen to them and wonder whether it can possibly happen again. The counselor has to advise himself when the antibodies that cause erythroblastosis in the child appear in the blood of his wife.

The bits and pieces above are but hints as to the complexities and kinds of problems that are presented daily at the Dight Institute.

More elaborate discussion of the problems that come to the heredity clinic, and short abstracts of the answers given, will be presented as individual chapters. It will not be possible to devote a chapter to every trait of interest to the counselor. The counselor encounters the most rare and bizarre situations because these are often new to the physician, and referral to the Dight Institute is highly probably. It is quite likely that we have seen a wider range of anomalies in the last 15 years at the Dight Institute than is ever seen by a single physician in his practice.

A listing of some of the rare traits the counselor may encounter is presented in the Appendix. The listing given in the first edition is now somewhat out of date, and it has been necessary to revise the list, item by item, in order that more recent references could be included. The new references will always permit the reader to work back to earlier ones. One look at the amazing array of defects or diseases shown in the Appendix should make us all want to pull up our socks and learn a little more about the vast field of medical genetics.

It will not be possible to give elaborate consideration even to the traits seen most frequently at the heredity clinic. The ones selected are not likely to appear equally often at different genetics centers. Above all, the frequencies of anomalies observed at the clinics are definitely *not* indications of the relative frequencies of these conditions in the general public. For example, Huntington's chorea provides a frequent counseling situation, even though only about 1 adult in 20,000 is affected. On the other hand, adult heart defects are the most frequent cause of death, yet there are seldom inquiries about the possible genetic aspects of cardiac problems. The selection of topics to be considered in subsequent chapters cannot be satisfactory to everyone, and it is not entirely satisfactory to me. The topics selected are representative of their counseling frequency, their teaching value and my own idiosyncracies.

There are problems other than those of the particular anomaly involved. There is also selection at the client level. There must be a fair amount of intelligence, insight and educational background behind the motivation that actually gets the client to the counseling center. Very few psychotics come to us. Our clients are usually in good mental health, have adequate incomes and are fairly well educated. The great majority of people coming to us are from the middle or upper classes. The counselors will belong to these same social classes and will be better able to communicate with the clients than would be the case if they were from indigent groups handled by welfare agencies. Genetic counseling is free so that the indigent may receive it, but they do not come for it in any appreciable numbers.

There is a difference between counseling the anxious parents of a defective child and satisfying the curiosity of high school students who wish to write a paper on human genetics. There is a continuous range of psychologic involvement between these extremes. I would not know where to draw the line in this continuum of involvement as to where counseling ends and only education is left. There is no reason for trying to make such a distinction. The counselor responds to the different situations by trying to help the client in any way that he can.

It is not only the parents of affected children who come for counseling. Adoption agency personnel bring babies for evaluation of their suitability for placement in adoptive homes. Premarital counseling is given young people whose marriage has been inhibited by their own anomalies or by their fear of the possible biologic results of consanguinity. The mother who does not wish her son to marry the girl of his choice comes to find genetic holes in the girl's armor. Lawyers want help in resolving paternity suits. The list of different kinds of clients is almost endless. The great range of variability in the kinds of genetic information desired emphasizes one point: the counselor must be a competent geneticist in order to do his job. It would be wonderful if he could also be a specialist in all fields from anthropology to zoology, including dentistry and medicine. Obviously, such versatility is impossible. The only solution is for the medical geneticist to solicit the aid and diagnoses of his colleagues. This assistance has always been given most graciously.

Genetic counseling has an enormous potential usefulness because about 1 in 50 of our children has some serious physical or mental problem due to genetic factors in an important degree. Even in cases where an anomaly is suspected of being the result of environmental causes, the geneticist will often be consulted. It is important to remember that some environmental causes of anomalies can be transmitted to subsequent children in the family just as specific unwanted genes might reappear in them.

The major problem of logistics for the genetic counselor of the future will be not to obtain clients but rather how to make genetic counseling available for all those who desire it.

Chapter 3

A PHILOSOPHY
FOR COUNSELING

Information about heredity, often incorrect, has been provided for families with abnormal children since the development of communication. The advice of friends, enemies and neighbors probably has been quite effective in altering the reproductive behavior of the family concerned. The most frequent ideas have been fortified by taboo status or even formal incorporation into religious dogma and civil law. A good number of states and nations have laws regulating consanguineous marriages, and most other reproductive behavior, which were taken directly from the Bible. Modern attitudes are greatly influenced by the collections of fact and fancy concerning human reproduction and heredity to be found in all sorts of religious writings. Many of these ancient declarations have been taken more literally than intended by their authors. Others have been so distorted that their modern versions do not have the validity of the original conceptions.

Since advice about heredity is certain to be given, it would seem that the physician or the professional geneticist is in a sounder position to give it than even one's best friend. The first requirement for the counselor, then, is some knowledge of human genetics. The second requirement—perhaps the most important—is that he have a deep respect for the sensitivities, attitudes and reactions of the client. A third requirement is the desire to teach, and to teach the truth to the full extent that it is known.

The primary function of counseling is to provide people with an understanding of the genetic problems they have in their families. It seems that almost every family has some troublesome situation directly related to the heredity of one or more of its members. Often the counselor can help alleviate the difficulties.

There may be quarreling between husband and wife as to the "blame" for an abnormality that has appeared in their child. A more dangerous situation exists when the resentment is present but is not expressed. The counselor is almost certain to be of help in these cases.

There may be a sense of shame due to the fact that hereditary diseases often carry social stigmata. Where recessive inheritance is concerned, it may be very helpful to point out that carrying a pathologic hereditary unit that is concealed by the normal unit does not mean that the carrier is defective himself. All of us probably carry several such hidden defects, and it is just bad luck when both parents happen to carry the same defect and produce a child showing the disease in the full-blown state. The patient will regain composure when he comprehends that hidden recessive genes are present, not only in his own germ plasm, but in the germ plasm of his friends, enemies and neighbors as well.

Maternal guilt is an emotional reaction that should be watched for, particularly when the child has a congenital defect. Sometimes the mother may not have wanted to have the baby. She may have made an unsuccessful attempt to abort it. Consequently, she may think that what is really an hereditary defect resulted from her action. Instruction as to the true cause of the defect will divert her attention and alleviate quite severe mental anguish.

The most frequent and most important function of the counselor is that of stating the chance of reappearance of an abnormality in each child subsequent to the affected one. The patient pays the physician for this information and is not getting his money's worth if he is only assured that "lightning never strikes twice in the same spot." In the families that came to us after the lightning had struck twice, the mistaken physician was no longer considered to be a family friend.

It has been our experience that one *can* explain to the parents what the chances are of another abnormal child and that they adjust to the facts very well. Being forewarned, they are psychologically forearmed if the next child does prove to have the abnormality. If the child is normal, they experience unusual gratitude and enjoy a mental uplift. In some of the cases that have come to our attention, in which the parents had not been conditioned to the possibility of a second abnormal child before it appeared, the mothers' mental structures were badly shaken. While we have helped to reorganize their psychologic shambles, it would have been better to have prevented the damage in the first place.

Our serious clients come to us because they are troubled. They show great affection for their abnormal child and give it more than its ordinary share of attention, but the parents are unhappy both for the defective child and for themselves. We have never seen parents who wished to repeat their misfortune. However, the desire to compensate for the loss of a child by the production of a normal baby is often very strong. So they want to know what the chances are of another abnormality. We give them the figure if we have a reliable one; otherwise, we tell them that we do not know the value. The parents often ask us directly whether they should have more children. This question is one that we do not answer because we cannot. The counselor has not experienced the emotional impact of their problem, nor is he intimately acquainted with their environment. We try to explain thoroughly what the genetic situation is, but the decision must be a personal one between the husband and wife, and theirs alone. Of course, if it is possible to help them, it should be done. Perhaps the most useful endeavor is that of merely explaining what chances are; many people do not understand what one chance in four amounts to, as an order of magnitude.

The decision the parents make may be either eugenic or dysgenic in regard to the hereditary trait under consideration. If they decide to have no more children, it is a eugenic decision; that is, they will not spread further their defective gene either through affected children or normal carriers. If, as is usually the case, the chances of producing another defective child are less than the parents feared, then they may have more children. This latter decision is dysgenic, since they will propagate the defective gene instead of arresting its spread. The over-all effect of genetic counseling is to encourage people to have more children than they would have had otherwise, since the chances of having bad luck are less than they had assumed (though usually vastly greater than the "one in a million" chance that may have been given them elsewhere). While it may seem that counseling is dysgenic in regard to the particular abnormal gene, it should be remembered that those people who are sufficiently concerned about the future to come for counseling have commendable concepts of their obligations as parents; morally speaking, these laudable characteristics should become more widespread.

A frequent question from interested nonclients of the Dight Institute concerns the relationship of counseling to religious precepts. Most religions have precepts which are intended to spell out the conditions according to which reproduction may take place. Some of the regulations have great significance, while others seem difficult to understand or are inconsistent. An example of the latter is the Hebraic prohibition against the marriage of an aunt and nephew, while the marriage of an uncle and niece is permitted. Genetically speaking, there is no difference between the two marriages.

There is no direct connection between genetic counseling and religious precepts. We do not answer the parents' question as to whether or not they should have more children. They must decide for themselves. It should be emphasized that the Dight Institute is not an antifertility clinic. One might ask what a Roman Catholic family would do if, as a result of genetic counseling, the couple decided not to have any more children. Presumably they would behave in the same way that millions of other Roman Catholics do who, for good reason, decide that their family is completed. In counseling cases where the chance of a normal child is small or nil, the Church would certainly approve the use of the rhythm method, since it is the intent that the method should be used for just such serious situations as this. With most women, the rhythm method will usually work if conscientiously employed. Nevertheless, the Dight Institute never gives information as to the methods of family planning, because that subject is outside its sphere of competence.

Let us conclude by pointing out that we can expect those who come for counseling to have a much more pessimistic view of their problem than the situation warrants. A most frequent question is "Can I expect to have any normal children?" Consequently, even the clumsiest counselor has an excellent chance of relieving the deep anxieties of his client. The counselor can also help to wash away the guilt feelings of the parents of the affected child by pointing out that genetic calamities can occur in any family and that the parents are not alone in their problem. One can influence the expression of his genes to an amazing degree, but no one can escape all the possible undesirable expressions of his genotype. It helps to remind the client who is suffering from self-blame or self-pity of the biblical phrase, "He maketh His sun to rise on the evil and on the good, and sendeth rain on the just and on the unjust."

Chapter 4

A FEW LAWS

The flood of information about human heredity that has taken place since 1900 is not due to the superiority of the scientists working today but rather to the fact that it was not until 1900 that the scientific world had laws at hand that described how heredity works and allowed predictions as to what might be expected in future generations. Most people know that the fundamental laws were discovered by Mendel, but few understand their implications or recognize the stupendous material gain that has resulted for all from the application of the laws to the improvement of our domesticated plants and animals. The laws are merely statements of the random assortment and recombination of the pairs of hereditary units present in the reproductive cells, so they apply to man in the same statistical fashion as they do to plants and animals. As the hereditary units, or genes, occur in pairs, the laws of heredity are based upon various manipulations of the number 2.

If the statistics are collected for all the children of a group of Huntington's chorea patients, it will be found that half of these children will also develop the disease when they reach the age for its appearance. No further cases will appear in the descendants of the normal children, but the affected persons will produce children half of whom eventually will be stricken with the disease. In each succeeding generation normal individuals will always produce normal offspring, but one-half of the offspring of the affected individuals, on the average, will develop the disease. Thus, the choreic passes his gene down through the generations. He marries normal persons and gives his gene for chorea to one-half of his children and his normal gene to the other half. The descendants who get the chorea gene from him and a normal gene from their mother will develop the disease because the chorea gene dominates the action of this pair of genes, which controls involuntary movements of the muscles. Because the defective chorea gene dominates its normal partner gene it is called a *dominant* gene or trait. The normal partner, which is suppressed or concealed by the chorea gene, is appropriately named a *recessive* gene.

The disease condition is not always dominant to the normal member of its own gene pair. Albinism is recessive to its normal gene, so the normal gene is dominant in this case. Since albinos usually marry normal people (if they marry at all), their offspring usually have normal pigmentation because the gene from the normal parent covers up the albino gene that the baby has received. Thus, the "carrier" child looks normal because his recessive albino gene has been covered up by its dominant normal partner. The only way in which the albino trait can emerge again is for the carrier to marry another carrier or an albino. A baby from this union will be an albino if it receives an albino gene from each parent. If both members of its gene pair for pigmentation are albino genes, the child will be an albino.

If both parents carry the gene for albinism, simple random combination of their normal and albino genes gives a predictable ration of albino and normally pigmented children. If the dominant gene for normal pigmentation be indicated by C and the defective gene for albinism be indicated by c, the carrier, who has both genes present in his body cells, is described, genetically, as Cc. The sperm produced by this carrier will have only one

member of the gene pair in each sperm. Half the sperm will have
C and the other half c. The same will be true for the eggs of
the carrier woman. When two carriers marry, the ratio of all
possible combinations of the C and c eggs and sperm will be
one CC child, two Cc children and one cc child. Because of the
dominance of the normal gene the CC child, without any gene
for albinism, cannot be distinguished by inspection from the two
carrier Cc children, who also look normal. The ratio we see is
three pigmented children to one albino. This 3:1 ratio was discovered by Mendel.

Mendel also discovered the 1:1 ratio, which would appear
in the children from the marriage of a carrier of albinism, Cc,
and an albino, cc. There are only two possible arithmetic combinations of genes from this marriage and they will appear in
equal numbers. Half of the children will be carriers, Cc, and
the other half albinos, cc. While the pathologic condition here
is *recessive* and comes about only when cc is the person's genetic
makeup, this 1:1 ratio also describes the marriage in which a
dominant pathologic condition, such as Huntington's chorea, has
been passed down from affected generation to affected generation. Thus, if the choreic is designated as Hh, he is not only a
carrier but also shows his disease. If he marries a normal woman,
hh, the ratio for their children will be one Hh, or choreic, to one
hh, or normal.

These extraordinarily simple 3:1 and 1:1 ratios defied discovery for over 2,000 years of "science," but once Mendel saw
the light, a new era of improved conditions for mankind began.

Mendel had large families of garden peas with which to
prove that, on the average, his ratios would appear. The families
of people whom the physician works with are much smaller than
the pea families. Obviously, a single fashionable two-child family
cannot by itself give a 3:1 ratio. Therefore, in medical genetics,
we have to pool data because of small family sizes, and this in-

troduces slight problems of arithmetic. If only people would be more considerate of the geneticist and always have at least 16 children, these arithmetic problems would not exist! Families of 16 or more children would be large enough to give mendelian ratios.

It should be emphasized that, while families are actually usually too small to give any good genetic ratios, the expectation for *each child* is always precisely that indicated by the appropriate genetic ratio. For instance, if a normal couple have had an albino child, they will know that they are carriers of the gene, and that, on purely statistical grounds, each subsequent child has a one out of four chance, that is, 25 per cent, of being an albino. The fact that they have already had an albino child tells them that they are carriers of the gene, but it is no insurance whatsoever against having any number of additional albino children. Each conception is an entirely independent event and is not genetically influenced by previous conceptions.

With a dominant trait, such as Huntington's chorea, the expectation for affected children of an affected parent will be 50 per cent for each child, in keeping with Mendel's 1 : 1 ratio.

These 25 and 50 per cent expectations for abnormal children are valid and are the values that the general practitioner should have in mind. The physician engaged in clinical research needs to have additional information as to the statistical problem, or bias, introduced in his data by the small family sizes. which have been deprecated above, facetiously, of course.

If children with a recessive difficulty such as fibrocystic disease of the pancreas are brought to a clinic for diagnosis and treatment, it should be clear that if the sick child is the first child in the family and has no brothers or sisters, then all such one-child families will be composed of nothing but sick children, or 100 per cent affected, instead of the 25 per cent from normal carrier parents assumed on mendelian grounds. This discrepancy is understandable because the carrier parents with only one normal child have no reason to appear at the clinic.

The family size of two children will permit families from normal parents to have one sick child and one normal child, or two sick children. Families with two normal children will have no reason to come to the clinic; because of their absence, the data will be biased away from the expected 25 per cent, and a total of 57.1 per cent sick children will be observed at the clinic. However, if by some chance carrier parents manage to have 16 children, it is practically certain that at least one child in all such families will have the disease, so every one of these mammoth families will appear at the clinic and they will average the 25 per cent sick children expected.

This means that the clinician who is doing research on a disease that has not previously been explored genetically must arrange his data according to family size or he will have little chance of detecting the type of heredity involved. A number of cases are known in which the scientist was so badly confused by the bias due to small family sizes that he declared that no genetics was involved. Later workers have showed clear-cut recessive or dominant heredity for the same data, merely by correcting for the family size bias. There are a number of ways of correcting for the bias. Perhaps the most appealing one for the clinician was devised by Madge Macklin, M.D. This method is known as the "Percentage Affected Expected." The details need not be considered here; if the clinician wishes to make a test for the type of heredity involved, he should consult a text in human genetics such as that by Stern (1960) for a more extensive treatment of the statistics than that given here. For the present, it should be sufficient to present the percentages of affected children that would be expected to appear at the clinic if both parents are carriers of a recessive and also if one is a carrier and the other a sufferer from the disease. The expected percentages of sick children for the carrier marriage, $Cc \times Cc$, are given first in Table II; the percentages for the carrier by affected parent marriage, $Cc \times cc$, are the second line of values.

It can be seen that the average expectation from the $Cc \times Cc$ marriages, the first line of values in Table II, is much above the 25 per cent usual mendelian expectation; the average percentage for the $Cc \times cc$ marriages is well above the 50 per cent mendelian expectation for large plant or animal families. The bias resulting from small human families makes a large pitfall, which we should circumvent with caution.

The laws which we have considered are not all those known to genetics, but they are basic and indispensable. There will be a few more laws slipped into later chapters. Do not worry about them, but please review the important points of the present chapter. Now that we have them well in mind, let's move on to a more lively subject, twins.

TABLE II   The Body of the Table Gives the Percentages of Sick Children Expected in Different Sized Families That Come to the Physician or Clinic

	Total Number of Children in the Family									
Parents	1	2	3	4	5	6	7	8	9	10
$Cc \times Cc$	100.0	57.1	43.2	36.5	32.8	30.4	28.8	27.7	27.0	26.5
$Cc \times cc$	100.0	66.0	57.0	53.4	51.5	50.8	50.4	50.0	50.0	50.0

Chapter 5

TWINS

The arrival of twins is usually a matter of mild consternation, mixed with a tingle of anticipation as to the interesting details of their future development. The tribes of upper Guinea look upon them with pleasure as an omen of fertility and plenty. In Australia the aborigines liquidate one of the twins; twins mean double trouble to them. Their view is that a woman can hardly expect to carry more than one child in her arms, because she has to carry her nomadic husband's spears and other belongings as well.

Twins appear in roughly 1 out of every 85 births, triplets in about 1 out of every 85 births squared, quadruplets in 1 out of every 85 births to the third power and quintuplets in 1 out of every 85 births to the fourth power. On March 26, 1952, Mrs. Alincia Bushnell Parker died at the age of 88. She was the last survivor of sextuplets born in Chicago during the Civil War. The well-known set of Dionne quintuplets was reduced to quadruplets by the death of Emilie on August 6, 1954. There is still one set of surviving quintuplets, the Diligenti quints of Argentina.

Aside from their interest as curiosities, twins are most valuable scientific material. As everyone knows, there are two kinds of twins, identical and fraternal. The identical twins start off as one egg fertilized by one sperm; the fertilized egg then separates into two identical parts. As the identical twins are merely one person walking around in two bodies, they must be genetically identical, gene for gene. Furthermore, they are forced into very similar environments, so that it is odd that they show any differences at all. Fraternal twins start as two separate eggs fertilized by separate sperm. They are no more alike, genetically, than ordinary brothers and sisters. They do share an environment that is more similar than that of ordinary brothers and sisters. There is no evidence that this somewhat greater similarity in environment makes a very profound difference in the expression of their measurable traits.

If all human traits behaved in the clear-cut mendelian fashion that albinism and Huntington's chorea do, twin studies would not be necessary as an aid in unraveling the complications that the environment often superimposes upon a mendelian pattern of heredity. There seems to be a rule that the most common defects have the largest environmental component, which makes it difficult to tell whether the hereditary basis for the abnormality is a simple dominant or recessive. The environment acts to suppress the expression of the abnormal gene in some cases but fails to do so in others. It can be appreciated that this unpredictable behavior of environmental factors would upset the classic orderly mendelian ratios, especially if they are the complicated ones that result when more than one gene pair is involved.

Pairs of twins are useful in detecting the relative effectiveness of heredity and environment upon the expression of a disease or trait. If a trait is highly hereditary, both members of a pair of identical twins will be expected to show the trait. If one identical twin shows the trait and the other member of the pair does not, the disagreement must be due to environmental differences between the two twins, because the genes of one are exactly the same as the genes of the other. Fraternal twins are no more alike genetically than ordinary siblings, so if they differ in that one twin has the abnormality and the other does not have it, one would not know whether it was the environment, the heredity, or both that differed for the two members of the pair. Actually, they differ in both their heredity and their environment. There are, of course, exceptions to these generalizations—but the general rules still hold.

We know that the heredity of blood groups behaves according to the mendelian rules and that environment seems to have no effect on the kind of blood group a person has. Consequently, with identical twins, both members of the pair will be expected to have exactly the same blood groups, and they always have. Fraternal twins frequently have different heredity for blood groups and therefore often disagree, or are discordant, even though we know that environmental differences have no hand in producing this discordance. Tuberculosis is a good example of a disease in which an hereditary susceptibility and an environmentally favorable situation are both necessary for the appearance of the active disease. A comparison of the behavior of identical and fraternal twin pairs for blood group, where heredity is all important, and for susceptibility to tuberculosis, where heredity and environment share the responsibility, is given in Table III. Notice how different the picture is for the two traits.

In Table III it can be seen that both members of the 125 pairs of identical twins agreed in having the same blood groups. The 91 pairs of fraternal twins showed 60 pairs in which both members had the same blood groups and 31 pairs in which the two members had different blood groups. The difference in susceptibility to tuberculosis of the two members of identical twin pairs is interesting. In 68 cases both got the disease but in 29 cases one of the identical twins got the disease while the other twin remained free of it. It is striking that there could have been sufficient difference in the environments of the two members of the identical twin pairs to cause one member to develop the disease and to permit the other to remain free of it. Both must have been genetically susceptible, as one of them was, but their environments differed enough so that one got the disease and the other did not.

In the following chapters data derived from twins will be presented, whenever possible, so that the reader can estimate how important environmental interference is in altering the appropriate mendelian ratios. Twins provide a rapid and easy first test for the presence of a genetic factor, and a study of them is helpful as a forerunner to a more detailed investigation with other methods.

A "cute" experiment reported by Kalmus (1955), of dogs trained to follow human tracks and to retrieve objects scented by people, showed that dogs can distinguish fairly reliably between the body odors of different individuals even when they are members of the same family. The individual odor of a person is perceived by the dog even when mixed with another person's body odor or with some strongly smelling substances. In retrieving experiments the body odors of identical twin partners are accepted for each other, and there is no indication that the dogs perceive any difference between them. It is probable that, when identical twins are together, these highly trained dogs can discriminate between them, which is better than most people can do.

The literature on identical twins raised apart is as fascinat-

TABLE III   The Contrast in Agreement and Disagreement between the Members of Twin Pairs, Identical and Fraternal, for Blood Groups and Susceptibility to Tuberculosis

| | Identical Twin Pairs | | Fraternal Twin Pairs | |
	Agree	Disagree	Agree	Disagree
Type of blood group	125	0	60	31
Susceptibility to tuberculosis	68	29	45	99

ing as anything one could read. A fairly recent article by Shields (1958) adds 38 pairs of identical twins reared apart to the many pairs for which the references are available in his citations.

Recently, we have been provided with a most interesting book on twins by Gedda (1961). This English summary of his work is highly recommended, as there is something of interest in it for everyone. The book is not only a thorough review of the twinning literature, but it is also enjoyable, the sign of any truly competent teacher.

In addition to the usefulness of twin pairs in shedding light upon the complicated interplay of heredity and environment, there are counseling questions to be answered.

The most frequent query concerns the heredity of twinning. Mothers who have had two or three pairs of twins themselves, and know of others among their close relatives, are certain that more than coincidence entered their lives. There is some evidence that twinning is hereditary, and, surprisingly enough, both identical and fraternal twins seem to result from the same heredity. As twins are common, it can be taken for granted that environmental factors influence their production or their failure to appear. There is no known mendelian ratio that applies to twins. The best that can be done is to confirm the mother's fears, or possibly hopes, that some weak tendency to twinning runs in families and that probably her chances of having twins are better than the chance of 1 in 85 found for the general population.

One of the papers concerned with the familial incidence of twinning is by Bulmer (1960). His conclusion is that the basis for twinning is to some extent genetic and that it is sex-limited, the father of the twins making no genetic contribution to them. While the heredity of the mother is of immediate significance in the production of twins, it should be remembered that about half of her heredity for twinning came from her father.

It will be the policy, in the remaining chapters of the book, to append at the end of the chapter one or more actual cases of counseling at the Dight Institute. These are merely shortened records, giving the essence of the problem and the main point of the answer. They should not be used as genetic cookbook recipes but should be helpful in providing the physician with background material necessary for his individual counseling cases.

The following case seems more trivial than it actually was. It is given to start our series of problems on a simple basis.

ILLUSTRATIVE EXAMPLE

Request.

A professor's wife of some 50-odd years of age had failed to have children. She had always considered her sterility to be due to the fact that she had a fraternal twin sister who did have children.

Reply.

The idea that one twin must be sterile is completely false, particularly in this case where both twins were of the same sex. It is probably a myth originating in rural communities where freemartins in cattle are well known. People are different from cows in many respects, including the placental situation that allows freemartins in cows but not in man. Furthermore, it is quite possible that the wife was normal and the husband the sterile partner. Even with sterility, husbands must accept the "blame" about half the time.

Chapter 6

THE UBIQUITOUS
HETEROZYGOTE

(*or, the Common Carrier*)

Typhoid Mary was a common carrier, but it was possible to isolate her from contact with foods and thus to remove her as a source of danger to the community. The carrier of a deleterious gene is not so easy to cope with. He is ubiquitous, he is everywhere. If every carrier of a recessive gene were isolated, there would be no further children and man would join his fossil ancestors. Don't worry—reproduction will not cease, even though everyone is a carrier of at least one recessive gene.

The scientific name for any carrier of a gene that is different from its partner gene is *heterozygote,* and the person is said to be *heterozygous* for the gene concerned. If both members of the gene pair are identical, the person is a *homozygote* and is said to be *homozygous* for the gene pair in question. Therefore, all that the formidable title of this chapter means is that people who are carriers of recessive genes, some of which are deleterious, are everywhere. It would seem that the writer is beating a willing horse. However, just be patient a moment and you will be surprised.

It is well known that universities grow because all the students bring some information *to* the university but few of them take much *away*. The one thing that would be most valuable for you to take away from this book is the concept of the ubiquitous heterozygote.

Let's illustrate the situation with our somewhat overworked example of albinism. If a couple discover that both marriage partners are heterozygous for the gene for albinism by producing an albino child, they should be told that the chance is one in four for each subsequent child that it will be an albino also. The longer the couple keep producing, the more certain they will be of getting at least one more albino child.

The frequency of albino births is 1 in every 15 to 20 thousand; let's be conservative and say it is 1 in every 20,000 births. Thus, any couple picked from the phone book is extremely unlikely to have had an albino child. This random couple has only 1 chance in 20,000 that their next child will be an albino, quite a different picture from that of the 1 in 4 chance for the couple both of whom are heterozygous.

Now the surprise! With a proportion of 1 in 20,000 of the population being homozygous, that is, albinos, what proportion of the population do you think is heterozygous for the albino gene? The answer is that 1 out of every 70 persons carries the gene for albinism! The next time you are at the circus just think of the number of heterozygotes sitting nearby under the big top, and remember that 1 in 70 is heterozygous for this particular gene, which, when homozygous, causes the really rare anomaly of albinism. A simple bit of arithmetic will show you that the heterozygote, or carrier of albinism, is 286 times more frequent than the albino himself.

How can we explain what seems to be an impossible situation? If as many as 1 out of every 70 people is heterozygous for albinism, why is it that only 1 out of every 20,000 people is an albino? We can work it out in this way. The chance that you, the reader, carry albinism is 1 in 70. The chance that your wife carries albinism is likewise 1 in 70. The chance that you both carry albinism is *not* the sum of these two values but is their product, which is 1 chance in 4,900! We must multiply this chance by another, the chance that, when you are both heterozygous, the child will be an albino rather than normal, and this is 1 in 4. The product of 1 in 4,900 times 1 in 4 is 1 in 19,600 or roughly the 1 in 20,000 births who is an albino.

The more rare the disease, the greater the disproportion between the frequency of carriers and affected persons. This is illustrated nicely in Table IV, which, for convenience, was taken from Stern (1960). The calculations were made by using what is known as the Hardy-Weinberg law. In a large population that has been stable for a long time, in which there is no consanguinity and in which there is no assortive mating for the pair of genes under consideration, the Hardy-Weinberg law would apply with precision. However, as no population ever satisfies these criteria, the law becomes only an approximation of varying exactness, though an extremely useful one.

The Hardy-Weinberg law states that there is a predictable relationship between the frequency of heterozygotes and that of the two homozygous classes. If the frequency of the normal gene, C, is indicated by the algebraic symbol p, and the frequency of the abnormal gene for albinism, c, is indicated by the algebraic symbol q, then the binomial expansion of $p + q$ gives the frequencies of the three genotypes in equilibrium. Thus, p^2 (CC, homozygous normals) : $2pq$ (Cc, heterozygotes) : q^2 (cc, homozygous albinos).

The genetic diseases that appear at the Dight Institute often enough to justify a chapter to themselves usually have frequencies greater than 1 in 1,000 births. If one recessive is necessary in the homozygous state for the disease to appear at all, we can see from Table IV that at least 1 out of every 16 people is heterozygous for this recessive gene.

The hosts of people who reject the idea that heredity has anything to do with mental and physical diseases do so because they do not understand the concept of the ubiquitous heterozygote. Over and over again, parents protest that the spina bifida in their child could not have had an hereditary basis because they know that nothing like it had come out in their families for the last three generations at least. A rare gene could have been passed down through their ancestors since the birth of Christ without having become homozygous. This point should be obvious, but it is a hard one to put across.

The most practical use for human genetics is in counseling. Unfortunately, at present most counseling occurs "after the fact." The couple has already produced a defective child and want to know the probability of having another. The child with the anomalies has proved the parents to be heterozygotes, carriers of the unwanted gene. It was an expensive way of providing this information. Ideally, genetic counseling should be premarital so that if a prospective couple should be carriers of the gene for a serious anomaly they could be steered toward other

TABLE IV   The Ratio of Carrier to Affected Individuals for Cases of Simple Single Factor Recessive Inheritance (after Stern, 1960)

Frequency of Affected Persons in the Population	Frequency of Carriers in the Population	Ratio of Carriers to Affected Persons
1 in 10	1 in 2.3	4.3:1
1 in 100	1 in 5.6	18:1
1 in 1,000	1 in 16	61:1
1 in 10,000	1 in 51	198:1
1 in 100,000	1 in 159	630:1
1 in 1,000,000	1 in 501	1,998:1

mates not so handicapped. But how can the carrier be detected before he has reproduced? It is a simple job to detect sickle cell anemia. It is merely necessary to examine a drop of the blood of any person; if he has the gene, the blood will sickle when deprived of oxygen. Two doses of the gene, which would be expected in one-fourth of the children from two carriers, produce the anemia, which is fatal. However, few diseases permit the detection of the genetic carriers this easily.

Neel (1953) has made a large contribution to human genetics in searching out ways of detecting the genetic carrier for various diseases. More recent information on chemical methods used in detecting heterozygosity has been assembled in an excellent text by Hsia (1959). The validity of determination of the carrier varies widely depending upon the trait considered. Presumably the physician should seek the advice of a geneticist if he wants to try to determine heterozygosity for any gene. We can now leave the ubiquitous heterozygote to his own devices, still undetectable in the majority of cases. Nonetheless, the day will come when a person can determine his heterozygosity with the reliability now provided by blood typing, we hope!

ILLUSTRATIVE EXAMPLE

Request.
    A physician delivered an albino child to a prominent young couple. They were much perturbed about the situation, but the physician told them that if the child were kept from the prying eyes of relatives and neighbors for a few months, it would darken up and everything would be fine. The couple received assurances that it was just an accident and could not happen to them again. After about a year the couple decided that some mistake had been made, as the child was still definitely an albino. They came to the Dight Institute.

Reply.
    As the young parents were intelligent and well educated in most respects, a short conversation was all that was necessary to ex-

plain both the chemistry and the genetics of albinism. Their confusion departed and they made their decision for the future on the spot, without further assistance. Their one in four chance of an albino at each subsequent pregnancy was an unpleasant surprise but one which they were able to comprehend and accept with fortitude.

Follow-up.

The albino child is now in his early teens and doing very well in every way. His nystagmus and vision difficulties have not prevented him from playing in the school band and enjoying some athletics. The parents, by intention, produced a normal boy who has been a tremendous pleasure to them, but it is unlikely that they will have any more children as the mother is close to menopause. Both parents are from very small families and would probably not have had many more than two children under any circumstances. It is possible that they might have had one or two more children than they did, if it were not for their clear understanding of their heterozygosity and its possible consequences.

Chapter 7

DON'T MARRY A
RELATIVE!

There is one advantage in marrying a blood relative; it simplifies your children's family tree. However, the disadvantages of consanguineous marriages may more than cancel this trivial advantage.

The union of relatives has been practiced throughout the ages. One looks upon the offspring of consanguineous arrangements with a quite unwarranted fascination, as if each such child were expected to be a modern Cleopatra or at least a two-headed monster. Whereas the marriage of close relatives has often been sanctioned by royalty, it has generally been taboo for commoners, and every sort of regulation has been enacted from the ridiculous to the sensible. The confusion has resulted from the general lack of understanding of how heredity works in the various degrees of relationship. Genetically, the only effect of consanguinity or incest is to produce, in full view in the offspring, those hidden traits coming from the ancestors common to the incestuous parents. These hidden traits may be beneficial or detrimental. They are likely to be detrimental more frequently than beneficial, and for this reason, if for no other, the union of relatives should be discouraged when possible. There are laws in many states prohibiting the marriage of close relatives, but the laws are not enforced and so are less effective than they might be.

The ordinary parent is not insistent that his children exceed him in strength of mind and body, advantages that could come from consanguinity; rather, he is anxious that his children not be mentally retarded or afflicted with some serious physical disability, disadvantages that could follow a consanguineous marriage. Thus, the value of the improvements that consanguinity might bring far from compensates for the anguish and trouble that would result if the child turned out to be defective rather than improved. Most people do not want to accept a proposition that involves a small chance of small gains and a large chance of large losses.

Twin studies are useful in indicating whether or not a condition has an appreciable genetic basis. Consanguinity is a second tool for the same work. It has the limitation that it is a critical test only for rare disabilities. However, for recessive uncommon abnormalities an unequivocal answer may be obtained. If family histories of a rare abnormality are collected and there is no evidence of dominance in them, we may generally expect that the anomaly is due to the double dose of a recessive gene. What is more, the parents of abnormal children must be blood relatives much more frequently than one would expect from population statistics. Lenz's law states, in effect, that the more rare a recessive gene in the population, the higher the rate of consanguineous marriages among the parents of affected children. This law is valid because very rare recessive genes, which are concealed in the whole population, will seldom be found in both members of a married couple. If, however, the parents are blood relatives, there will be a reasonable chance that both will be carrying at least one of the deleterious recessives possessed by one or more of their common ancestors. Thus, by having children by a blood relative, one increases tremendously the chances that a recessive, which has been carried concealed down through the generations, will become expressed in the effective double dose in the children.

Muller (1950) estimated that the average person carries about 8 deleterious mutations in the concealed condition. It is unlikely that your wife would also carry any one of these same 8 rare recessives, though she would carry 8 others of her own. If two of your grandchildren marry (they would be first cousins), there is 1 chance in 16 that both would carry a particular one of the 16 recessives carried by your wife and you. The chance that both grandchildren would not carry the same recessive is $\frac{15}{16}$, and the chance that they would both fail to carry the same one of *any* of the 16 different recessives possessed by your wife and you is $(\frac{15}{16})^{16}$, or 0.356. Consequently, the probability that any two of your grandchildren would both carry at least 1 identical gene out of the 16 assumed for the grandparents is equal to $1-(\frac{15}{16})^{16}$, or 0.644. The probability that the first product of a first cousin marriage would be homozygous for a particular one of the recessives carried by both his parents is one-fourth of 0.644, or 0.161. Should the first cousin families all have four offspring, 0.644 of these families, on the average, should have produced at least one person homozygous for a detrimental recessive. Don't marry a relative!

This frightening picture can be tempered somewhat by pointing out that Muller did *not* imply that the 8 detrimental genes of his estimate were all concerned with congenital or childhood abnormalities. They were assumed to have their effect upon the individual at any time from conception until the age of 100 years or more. If we take a wild guess and arbitrarily consider that one-fifth of the 16 detrimental genes of the grandparents are capable of producing congenital or childhood anomalies, then $\frac{1}{5}\times0.161$, or 0.032 (1 in 31), of the first cousin marriages should produce a congenital or childhood abnormality in the first child, or 1 in 8 of the first cousin marriages should produce such an anomaly if at least four children are achieved in each family.

More recent studies by Morton (1960) and Freire-Maia

(1960) augment Muller's concepts about consanguinity and give more refined mathematical treatments of more extensive data, which indicate that the average person carries heterozygously the equivalent of three to five recessive lethals acting between late fetal and early adult stages.

Among the general population, in spite of laws to the contrary, about one-half of 1 per cent of all marriages seem to be contracted between first cousins. A somewhat higher percentage of marriages might be expected between more distant relatives, but the total percentage of consanguineous marriages of all degrees would not begin to approach the high figure observed among the parents of children having rare recessive defects. In Table V are some examples of hereditary rare diseases in which recessive inheritance is indicated by the phenomenally high number of first cousin marriages among the parents of the affected children.

The counselor will be asked about the practical results of consanguinity. Table V shows that for five rare diseases the proportion of affected children whose parents were first cousins is from 11 to 47 per cent. Had these consanguineous marriages not occurred, the population of children with rare diseases would have been reduced by from about one-tenth to one-third, cer-

TABLE V   Abnormally High Rate of First Cousin Marriages among the Parents of Children with Some Rare Diseases

Disease	Per Cent First Cousin Marriages among the Parents
Wilson's disease	47
Alkaptonuria	33
Xeroderma pigmentosa	26
Congenital ichthyosis	24
Albinism	17
Total color blindness	11

tainly a prevention of misfortune which society ought to insist upon more vigorously. For its own protection, society as a whole should attempt to prevent the marriage of relatives, or at least the production of children by close relatives. If this is the obvious stand for society, what is the situation for the individual couple? How much are the chances of having an abnormal child increased by the marriage of relatives, as compared with marriages of nonrelatives?

Studies here and abroad have shown that approximately 1 in every 65 newborn infants has a gross malformation. This value is for the general population. A number of good studies on the increased mortality and abnormalities found for offspring of cousin marriages have been published for populations in France, Japan, Sweden and the U.S.A. The reader is referred to Chapter 19 of Stern (1960) for an interesting synthesis of the work in this field. It is clear that the risk of a congenital abnormality in the child from a first cousin marriage is about twice that expected for children from a marriage of nonrelatives. If nonrelatives have a 1½ per cent chance that their first child will have a major defect, we would expect that first cousins would have a 3 per cent chance of their child having an abnormality of brain or body. The extremely limited data from our counseling experience at the Dight Institute indicate that the child resulting from a brother-sister union has about a 10 per cent chance of presenting some anomaly.

The usual counseling case involves first cousins or more distant relatives. The increased risks do not seem large enough to warrant taking a firm stand against the marriage of first cousins, yet they flirt with danger rather needlessly when one realizes that these people could marry nonrelatives. Marrying a relative could only be justified if it were not possible to find as satisfactory a mate among the much greater mass of nonrelatives.

The counselor does not tell the boy and girl that they

should not marry; he points out the dangers and also the fact that in Minnesota and many other states it is illegal for persons more closely related than second cousins to marry. The number of states in which the marriage of first cousins is legal has decreased recently. Table VI lists the states in which first cousin marriages seem to be legal. It is of interest to those couples who have already decided to marry and wish to avoid the local law. In Wisconsin, marriage between first cousins is permitted if the woman has reached the age of 50.

TABLE VI   States in Which the Marriage of First Cousins Would Seem to Be Legal (the Attorney General Should Be Written to in Each Case)

Alabama	New Mexico
California	New York
Connecticut	Rhode Island
District of Columbia	South Carolina
Florida	Tennessee
Maine	Texas
Maryland	Vermont
Massachusetts	Virginia
New Jersey	

ILLUSTRATIVE EXAMPLES

1.   *Request.*

A teen-age brother and sister of one of the "best" families in the Twin Cities had been so carefully shielded from the viciousness of the outside world that they were completely innocent of any sex education whatever. At least, they were able to convince the social worker that they had no idea that a baby might result from their sexual intercourse. The girl took a trip to a maternity home and arranged with a welfare group to have the baby placed for adoption when it was born. The welfare group wanted to ascertain the possibility that the child might turn out to be abnormal.

Reply.

There is at least 1 chance in 100 that *any* birth will yield a child that is abnormal in some way. The chance that this baby will be abnormal in some particular is greater than 1 in 100 because it is reasonable to suppose that the common ancestors of the parents carried some hidden deleterious recessives, which may come out in this child. Unfortunately, we do not yet have the research figures that would allow us to predict the risk of an abnormality from brother-sister unions.

First Follow-up.

The baby had a mildly deformed clubfoot, which apparently was not considered difficult to correct. A professional couple was happy to adopt the baby with a full understanding of the circumstances of its birth. The baby adjusted very well and has developed nicely. The couple now wants to adopt another child to round out the family. Thus, a story that started as a needless result of social stupidity came to a fairly happy ending.

Second Follow-up.

The "baby" is now a well-developed school child. The only disappointment so far is that her I.Q. is only 95, lower than we had expected under the circumstances.

2.   *Request.*

A sailor and his girl friend were first cousins once removed and had the same last name. They wanted to know what the risk for their potential children might be. The sailor had an unusually fine personality and seemed highly intelligent. In addition, he appeared to have a larger supply of hormones than even the average sailor and was all for getting married—if a state could be found where it would be legal. The girl was more cautious.

Reply.

The doubling of the risk of an abnormal child for full first cousins was explained and the impossibility of a legal marriage in Minnesota pointed out. The list of states in which their marriage might be legal was presented to them and is reproduced in Table VI. It was emphasized that the counselor is not a lawyer and that they should check with the attorney general of any state they might choose from the list.

First Follow-up.

The girl came back again alone a few days later to go over the same material again. It was clear that she had grave doubts as to the wisdom of marrying her cousin, even though they were both greatly attracted to each other.

Second Follow-up.

Many months later the counselor phoned the girl to find out how they were progressing. The reply was that they had thought about the problem seriously for a long time and had decided that the combination of the legal aspects and the risks for any children they might have was too troublesome. Everything was finished; they were disengaged and no longer were in contact with each other.

3.   *Request.*

An unusually gifted young physician was determined to marry his mother's half sister. The girl was only two years his senior. The physician's mother and father came with him for counseling, as the mother objected to her son marrying her half sister although she did not object to the idea of first cousin marriages as such. The physician was concerned only with the chances of the marriage resulting in defective children.

Reply.

It was pointed out to the mother that the situation was genetically the same as that for first cousin marriages.

Follow-up.

Numerous contacts have been made with the physician, who married his half-aunt as expected in California. They have produced three children, who are normal.

Chapter 8

THE CHROMOSOME
BREAK-THROUGH

It is amazing how long opportunity must sometimes knock at the door before anyone will answer. The lag between stimulus and response is shown clearly in the field of human chromosome study. The tremendous importance of human chromosome work has only become apparent during the last few years, although the theoretical foundations for the recent break-through were published long ago.

Many years ago A. F. Blakeslee showed that the plant *Datura stramonium* has 12 pairs of chromosomes. It was possible to obtain plants that had an extra chromosome present in their cells. If the extra chromosome present was a member of the fourth pair, for instance, there would be three fourth chromosomes in each cell of the plant and we would say that the plant was a *trisomic* for the fourth chromosome. The presence of three fourth chromosomes with only two chromosomes for each of the other 11 pairs in each cell upsets the gene balance and inevitably produces an abnormal plant. The abnormality is distinctive and reproducible. If it is the seventh chromosome that is present in the triple condition rather than the fourth, a different and easily recognizable abnormality will be produced. It was found that the trisomic for each of the 12 pairs of chromosomes resulted in a different anomalous type of plant, and as there are 12 of these variants, it is only natural that they are referred to as "Blakeslee's apostles."

One might have expected that he would have also found 12 different monosomics, each having lost 1 of the 12 chromosomes of the normal set, but such monosomics in *Datura* are inviable and do not appear.

Man has 23 pairs of chromosomes and therefore should produce at least 23 different trisomic abnormal types. No one grasped this important concept upon the publication of Blakeslee's work with plants in 1934. Indeed, it can be stated with shame that we didn't even know that the correct number of chromosomes in man is 46, that is, 23 pairs, until 1956. The number had previously been thought to be 48.

The spark that ignited the present interest in human cytology was provided first by Lejeune, Gautier and Turpin in January, 1959, when they showed that three boys with the mongolism syndrome had a small extra chromosome. In England similar work was in progress, and in the same year Jacobs and Strong (1959) first reported a patient with gonadal dysgenesis of the Klinefelter type with an extra X chromosome, thus giving a person with an XXY chromosome an anomaly that results in intersexuality. The trisomy here is for the pair of sex chromosomes, and it permits another trisomic for this pair of chromosomes with equal ease. The second sex-chromosome trisomic expected would be XXX, and this type of female has been found. Much more remarkable, two cases of XXXX females have been found. These XXX and XXXX females are not easy to spot clinically, although a study of buccal smears mirrors the chromosome picture, in that there is always one less chromatin body in the smears than the number of X chromosomes. The buccal smears are interesting, but they give no information not available from a study of the chromosomes themselves and should never be considered a valid substitute for the chromosome studies. The multiple-X females are often mentally retarded but often fertile, and at least half of the offspring of the XXX females will be genetically and phenotypically normal. At least two cases of XXXXY males have been reported in the literature, the more recent by Miller, Breg, Schmickel and Tretter (1961). These are very poorly developed males and seem to be sterile and mentally retarded.

It is not likely that a viable monosomic YO child will ever be found, but the XO monosomic is abundant. This condition is known as Turner's syndrome. The XO female has short stature, almost always associated with streak gonads and primary amenorrhea and often with neck webbing, coarctation of the aorta and digital anomalies.

Thus we have the normal XX female and the normal XY male and, in addition, not just one trisomic and one monosomic but a constellation of different sex-chromosome anomalies and various mosaic combinations of normal and anomalous numbers of sex chromosomes in one individual. Those interested in this field of sexual abnormalities should read the summary by Harnden and Jacobs (1961). It is by no means the last word on the subject, but it shows so clearly how far we were from any understanding of the etiology of sexual abnormalities before the chromosome break-through occurred.

In the family reported above (Miller et al.), there was also a leukemic male and two 21st-chromosome trisomic females. Early in the explosion of chromosome studies an individual was found with 48 chromosomes who had XXY (Klinefelter's syndrome) and 21st-chromosome trisomy (Down's syndrome—mongolism). In families with multiple chromosomal anomalies it may be that there is a predisposition to meiotic nondisjunction.

It seems reasonable to expect that the presence of an

extra chromosome would result in both physical and mental anomalies. The physical defects produced are not the same for the different trisomics, and it is not to be expected that the mental anomalies are identical either. Most of the mental anomalies resulting from chromosomal aberrations have been described generally as "mental retardation," but this is presumably because we are unable to classify many of the genetically different but phenotypically similar types of mental retardation.

At least two further types of autosomal trisomy syndromes are recognized in addition to those involving the sex chromosomes and the classic case of Down's syndrome (mongolism). Perhaps more of the autosomal trisomic varieties will be found, as there are 22 pairs of autosomal chromosomes, each of which could have its distinctive trisomic anomaly. One of the trisomic anomalies depends upon the triple condition of chromosomes of pair 17 or 18 and produces low-set malformed ears and micrognathia as well as mental retardation—the conditions that distinguish this syndrome (Edwards, Harnden, Cameron, Crosse and Wolff, 1960). The other trisomic anomaly is of chromosomes 13 to 15 and is expressed as mental retardation and a serious eye defect (Therman, Patau, Smith and Demars, 1961). The above individuals are not members of law firms, but they are good illustrations of the successful teamwork that results when an important problem-solving technique such as human chromosome study appears on the scene.

One could find many possible types of chromosomal aberrations in addition to the excess or deficiency of whole chromosomes. Chromosomes from different pairs may come in contact with each other and exchange pieces. This exchange may result in two chromosomes of unequal length. One may have almost all of the material from both original chromosomes while the other is composed of the remaining fractions. The latter product of the reciprocal translocation would be grossly deficient in genetic material, and the daughter cell containing it might be eliminated. The longer complementary translocated chromosome might survive through a few human generations, but it would give abnormal offspring and we would expect it to be eliminated eventually. Such translocations involving the 21st pair of chromosomes are occasionally responsible for Down's syndrome and will be considered in the next chapter. Moorhead, Mellman and Wenar (1961) have reported on a translocation between what appear to be chromosomes 13 and 22, which was present in a mother and four of her six offspring. The associated defects were predominantly lack of speech and mental retardation.

One of the most stimulating areas in human cytology concerns the relationship between neoplasms and chromosomal aberrations. Assaults on this problem have had rather equivocal results, but the data regarding the leukemias are at least highly intriguing. My colleagues Krivit and Good (1956) were the first to insist that there is more than a coincidental association between mongolism and acute leukemia. They pointed out that the relationship between these diseases must be an essential one, deserving of detailed consideration. Their observations were confirmed by Stewart, Webb and Hewitt (1958). The discovery that mongolism results from the trisomy of the 21st pair of chromosomes added interest because it immediately related acute leukemia to the 21st-chromosome trisomy in some mysterious way.

A recent paper by Graham (1960) reviews the literature concerned with the high frequency of myeloid leukemia appearing in patients after x-ray therapy for ankylosing spondylitis. The deaths occurred from about eight months to eight years after the treatment. It is common knowledge that leukemia was the most frequently delayed response in persons irradiated during the Hiroshima and Nagasaki atomic bombings. One of the obvious results of the irradiation of living cells is the breakage of one or more chromosomes.

Tough, Baikie, Harnden, King, Court-Brown, Buckton, Jacobs and McBride (1961) tied some of the data together and pointed out that myeloid leukemia patients usually can be shown to have what is called the "Philadelphia" chromosome present in some of their leukocytes but not in skin cells. This could indicate that the Philadelphia chromosome is the 21st chromosome that has lost perhaps a third of its length, and that it multiplies in the person at a greater rate than the normal chromosome partner. Eventually, the excess of white cells, many of them with the Philadelphia chromosome, produces the symptoms of *chronic myeloid* but *not acute* leukemia. There is no evidence that fragmented chromosomes of pairs other than the 21st result in leukemia. Their conclusion is that the 21st chromosome "may carry on it a genetic locus concerned with leucopoiesis."

My summary of the possible situation is that triplication of the gene locus, as in mongolism, gives increased liability toward *acute* leukemia, while a deletion of the locus, as seen in the Philadelphia chromosome, is responsible for most cases of *chronic myeloid* leukemia.

It should be clear from the examples so briefly considered above that human cytology will reveal most unexpected discoveries in medicine as our techniques improve and as laboratories for routine clinical human cytology are established in hospitals and medical centers.

ILLUSTRATIVE EXAMPLES

Requests for chromosome preparations for all sorts of patients flooded the Dight Institute as physicians learned about the chromosome break-through. It is a pleasure to thank my graduate student, Robert C. Goodlin, M.D., as well as Patricia Baker and Dr. Gerhard Brand who came to my rescue and performed the human chromosome technique again and again. The results from their studies gave a finesse to counseling that could not have been obtained in any other way. The effects of counseling, with the photography of the person's chromosomes on hand, are still too recent to evaluate, although the pictures certainly give new life to old problems. It came as no surprise that many physicians wanted chromosome studies made for ordinary mendelian traits. It is sometimes a little embarrassing to refuse these studies, when not indicated, as apparently pictures are much more satisfying than the 3:1 ratio of Mendel, no matter how well it works.

We now have a chromosome laboratory established in the Department of Laboratory Medicine, University of Minnesota, under the direction of Dr. Jorge Yunis. It provides the basic data for counseling with greatly increased accuracy in many cases.

Chapter 9

DOWN'S SYNDROME
(MONGOLISM)

It has been realized for a long time that mongolism is not an appropriate term for this complex of symptoms. The term is not particularly descriptive, and when the syndrome appears in Asians, such an ambiguous designation as "mongol mongoloid" results. My opinion is that "congenital acromicria" is the best scientific designation but I doubt that the general public would ever adopt this term in place of the word "mongolism." It is helpful if scientists and the general public use the same terminology, and it is my prediction that "Down's syndrome" is the term most likely to replace the word "mongolism," if a replacement occurs. A group of geneticists have suggested "Down's syndrome" as a possible replacement in the April 8, 1961, issue of *The Lancet.*

Down's syndrome is one of the more frequent types of congenital anomalies, particularly when one realizes that some children with the syndrome are not diagnosed before they leave the hospital where they were born or because of early death due to heart defects, which are very frequent in these children. Böök and Reed (1950) published excellent data collected by Böök in three North Sweden parishes. A census of the whole population showed that 1 in every 435 children under 20 years of age had Down's syndrome. Öster (1953) stated that in Denmark 1 child in every 618 born alive had the syndrome. If one could include the loss of undiagnosed affected babies, the frequency would certainly be in the neighborhood of 1 affected per 500 births.

In 1955, when the first edition of this book was published, the following statement was included, and it is of interest today.

"The etiology of mongolism is thoroughly confused. Practically every toxic agent has been indicated as the cause. Obviously much of this kind of evidence is pure coincidence. The endocrines seem to be related to the picture but their mode of action is not clear. Some writers have stated flatly that mongolism is not affected by any hereditary taint. This may be true but it is very difficult, and generally unpromising, to attempt to show that one can ignore the effects of the genes, all of which are necessary for every cell.

"It is reasonable to assume that there is a relationship between the genes in the cells and mongolism."

It could have been added that not only are all the genes necessary but they are necessary in the proper balance. If the genes of one of the smallest chromosomes (21st pair) are present in an extra set in the egg, a child with Down's syndrome will result. The exciting discovery by Lejeune, Gautier and Turpin (1959) that trisomy for the 21st pair of chromosomes is the basic cause of Down's syndrome was reported in the previous chapter.

Data derived from twins always supported a strong genetic hypothesis for Down's syndrome, but it is not necessary to repeat them here because the new cytologic picture is entirely convincing. Furthermore, there are now sufficient cases known in which girls with Down's syndrome have reproduced to demonstrate directly that the syndrome is hereditary in the strict sense. A review by Thompson (1961) indicated that 10 girls with the syndrome produced seven normal and five affected children. This is almost as close to a 1:1 ratio as one could get and shows that half of the eggs produced by a girl with Down's syndrome receive the extra chromosome and half do not. The eggs with the extra 21st chromosome give rise to offspring with the syndrome, as would be expected. The fact that the person with Down's syndrome seldom reproduces does not make the trait any less hereditary in those who do have a child. It is merely because the symptoms of the disease are so severe that it is not transmitted generation after generation but usually arises anew as a result of meiotic nondisjunction in a normal parent.

A study was made by Stearns, Droulard and Sahler (1960) of the reproductive potentials of institutionalized persons with Down's syndrome. In the females menses were comparatively normal between ages 16 and 46. In males, five patients had grossly subnormal sperm counts, with complete absence of sperm in four others. Ten patients were unable to produce an ejaculation and two were unable to maintain an erection. It is clear that in males, even more than in females, the presence of the small extra 21st chromosome is almost invariably a genetic lethal.

It has been known for many years that the risk of producing a child with Down's syndrome climbs steeply in older mothers. This is of concern to normal women who become pregnant toward the end of the reproductive period. Öster (1953) showed that if all women avoided pregnancies after the age of

TABLE VII   Percentage Risk Figures for the Incidence of Affected Children Expected from Mothers of Different Ages

	Age of Mother						
	15–20	20–24	25–29	30–34	35–39	40–44	45–49
Carter and MacCarthy	0.00	0.03	0.03	0.17	0.35	1.42	2.63
Oster	0.06	0.07	0.07	0.11	0.36	1.03	1.78

40, the incidence of children with Down's syndrome could be reduced by about 30 per cent. It is common practice for the physician to advise his patient to have her children before the end of the reproductive period approaches. The observations by Öster and by Carter and MacCarthy (1951) shown in Table VII support the physician's empirical conclusion.

It is distressingly clear from the table that older mothers run an appreciable risk of producing a child with Down's syndrome. For any woman over 45, the chance of producing an affected child is in the neighborhood of 1.8 to 2.6 per cent, and these values are probably a little low because of diagnostic difficulties.

Why does this relationship between age and greater nondisjunction of the 21st chromosome exist? We don't know the answer. It is the primary problem in the prevention of Down's syndrome. At least one-third of the cases could be prevented if the mother completed her family before she was 40. It is practical and sensible to do this from every point of view. The more difficult question of how to prevent nondisjunction for any pair of chromosomes has hardly been considered yet, but it merits attention because of the other anomalies, as well as Down's syndrome, that result from chromosomal nondisjunction. The size of the problem becomes clear when one realizes that of about 4,000,000 births per year in the United States alone, some 8,000 infants will have Down's syndrome!

A recent review by Rowley (1962) showed that of 47 children with Down's syndrome for whom chromosome studies were done, 40 had the usual extra 21st chromosome present and 7 children had some other arrangement. Most workers no longer take the trouble to report the affected children with the usual 21st-chromosome trisomy; therefore, the proportion of seven exceptions is too high, as most of the exceptions can be expected to appear in the literature. However, the exceptions strengthen the chromosome hypothesis greatly. It is found in the exceptional cases that the extra chromosome is present even though the affected child has the normal count of 46 chromosomes. The extra, or 47th, chromosome is attached to one of the other pairs. This results from what is called a reciprocal translocation.

The counseling problem is quite different in the usual freely segregating extra 21st chromosome situation from that for the rare family in which the extra chromosome is translocated to a member of another pair. The translocated 21st chromosome may also be found in a person who has only one free 21st chromosome and hence is normal, although the chromosome *count* will be only 45. This normal-appearing person can transmit the translocated 21st and a free 21st chromosome together to his or her child, and it will be affected with Down's syndrome, as the third 21st chromosome will come from the other parent. The risk of an affected child from a normal-appearing person having the translocated chromosome is 25 per cent, or 33 per cent if a further consideration is taken into account. It is not appropriate to devote space here to a more detailed description of the chromosome segregation of the translocated 21st chromosome. The reader is referred to Carter, Hamerton, Polani, Gunalp and Weller (1960) for such a description and a diagram of this interesting variation in the chromosome picture.

It should be mentioned that not all families with more than one child with Down's syndrome will have the translocated 21st chromosome present. Sometimes a second child will have the usual free 21st-chromosome trisomy; this could be purely coincidental, or it might be due to some other cause. The proportion of families in which a translocated 21st chromosome is present compared with those in which the second affected child has the usual trisomy is of interest. Forssman and Lehmann (1962) studied 11 families with more than one affected child and found that the extra 21st chromosome was translocated in 3 of them and free in 8.

A recent paper by Hamerton et al. (1961) is of great interest, although one should be conservative about the conclusion drawn, as the authors no doubt are. They present a family of 16 persons, 15 of whom show the translocation of the 21st chromosome to one of those in the D group, leaving only one person without it where we would expect several normals. The authors suggest that only the translocated chromosome is transmitted through the sperm. However, more data are needed before the conclusion is accepted.

A further complication has been found in other rare individuals in whom some of the body cells have the extra 21st chromosome and others do not. These chromosomal mosaics are no surprise to the geneticist. They succeed in confusing the diagnosis and create a difficult problem in trying to determine their frequency. Clarke, Edwards and Smallpiece (1961) have presented a most interesting case of a girl with mosaicism for Down's syndrome.

Carter and Evans (1961) have presented data on the sibs of 642 index patients with Down's syndrome. Of 312 sibs born after the index patient, 5 also had the anomaly whereas only 1 would have been expected from the prevalence in the general population. For mothers under 25 years of age the risks are something like fiftyfold the random risk; for mothers of 25 to 34 years the risks are fivefold the random risk; no increase in risks is apparent for mothers over 35. In part, at least, the explanation of these findings is that some young mothers of children with Down's syndrome, but rarely older mothers, run a high risk of a second affected child because either they or their husbands have a chromosomal abnormality. The fiftyfold increase just mentioned may sound rather frightening, but it should be realized that this comes about because the two affected children observed for mothers under 25 are 50 times the number expected by chance, which is only 0.039 of a child.

Let us summarize the counseling situation for Down's syndrome, as it is slightly complicated. It is obvious that if a chromosome study can be carried out on the affected child and the parents, it will be helpful for counseling.

a. The most frequent situation will be one in which the mother is over 35 years of age and the child has the free extra 21st chromosome. This mother will have about the same chance of having another affected child as any other woman of her age. Generally, she will not desire more children, partly because she is approaching the end of her reproductive life.

b. Most younger mothers with an affected child will also have about the same chance of producing another affected child as the generality of women of their age. Most will wish to take the small chance of another affected child. However, if the child has the extra 21st chromosome in the translocated form, the counseling picture changes drastically. Now the chances of another affected child increase to 25 or 33 per cent, and at this level most parents would hesitate, at least, before further intentional reproduction.

c. In the case of a mosaic, in which some cells of the body have the extra 21st chromosome and other cells do not, the expert will probably be baffled. He will be most interested and should be given the opportunity to struggle with his confusion.

Early detection of Down's syndrome is important for the welfare of the entire family. It is unfair for the family to have to go through months of worry and suspense while waiting for a diagnosis when there is doubt whether the child has Down's syndrome. A study of the child's chromosomes can easily and definitely resolve the issue in most of the doubtful cases.

ILLUSTRATIVE EXAMPLES

1.   *Request.*
         A student in my classes explained that he has three children,
two of whom are mongoloid. He came to the office, apparently with
some questions in mind, but the emotional aspects of the situation
seized him so abruptly that he hustled out without stating the
questions.

     Reply.
         There was none. In spite of good student-teacher rapport he
never mentioned the subject again. Nor did the writer attempt to
intrude.

2.   *Request.*
         A war veteran student had just become the father of his first
child, a mongoloid. He had received unsatisfactory answers from a
number of professional people before coming to the geneticist. His
sexual outlet during his army experience had been restricted to masturbation. His question was "Is my mongoloid child a result of some
hereditary peculiarity of my wife or due to the masturbation?"

     Reply.
         The undesirable sex practice could not be expected to be
relevant. It was pointed out to him that on his right hand he had a
transverse crease, a peculiarity found more often in mongols and their
blood relatives than in the general population. When it became clear
to him that there was some kind of hereditary background involving
him, his attitude toward the problem eventually became matter of fact
and his reproach for his wife and his own feelings of guilt disappeared.

3.   Mrs. J. has a niece with almond-shaped eyes but who is otherwise normal. This girl has five younger sibs, none of whom are
mongoloid.

                Mrs. J. gave birth to a normal boy at the age of 25 and to a
daughter, a mongoloid, at age 28. This child is still alive at 13. The
next child was a normal boy. After counseling at the Dight Institute
and an appreciation that she invited some risk at the age of 40, Mrs. J.
decided to have one more child and wanted a normal girl intensely.
This child did turn out to be a girl, and apparently a name had been
picked for her before birth. The first name differed from that of the
mongoloid daughter by only the last letter; the middle name was Hope.
The mother's disappointment must have been excruciating, because
the little girl was another mongoloid and in addition had a lobulated
tongue and cleft palate. She died at six months.

4.   A 23 year old mother gave birth to a mongoloid boy, then to a normal girl, and at age 29 to her third child, a mongoloid girl. Before the birth of her second mongoloid, the mother had been assured by two physicians that there was no danger of an affected child. Without warning, the second abnormal child was presented to the mother, with resulting psychologic trauma, the mother having made the diagnosis herself. After a period of adjustment to this shock, the couple appeared for counseling.

Upon examination of the hands of the couple, the husband showed a striking transverse crease of the left hand and a less pronounced demonstration of it on the right hand. Both could see this clearly. The wife's hands were normal.

Request.
        "What are the chances of our having a third mongoloid child?"

Reply.
        The transverse crease on the hands of the husband suggests that there is something more than accident concerned with the production of the rather uniform entity of mongolism. Consequently, there is a small chance that a third mongoloid child might result from another pregnancy. If another pregnancy is to be attempted, the couple must prepare for the small, but real, chance of a third mongoloid child.

Follow-up.
        Since the counseling, another child has been born. The parents, though prepared for the worst, had an uneventful pregnancy and were both relieved and delighted that it resulted in a normal boy.

Second Follow-up.
        The couple now have their fifth child, a normal. Score: three normals to two mongoloids.

It has not been possible to study the chromosomes of the families just described as yet because of more pressing cases involving young mothers who have produced children with Down's syndrome. These mothers usually wish to have more children, and it is important to be certain that the child has the free extra 21st chromosome and not an extra chromosome of the translocated type. Once this has been determined, the parents can be informed that their chromosomes appear to be normal and that the mother has no greater likelihood of having another child affected with Down's syndrome than any other woman of her age. This may be slightly optimistic but it is within the correct order of magnitude. It is remarkable how extremely pleased and relieved the parents are to learn that their chromosomes are normal. There is no question that the parents who have had an abnormal child indulge in some degree of self-survey. They appreciate the washing away of guilt feelings that the chromosome study so clearly provides.

It is too soon to report on the cases counseled for the threatening situation that resulted when the 21st chromosome was of the translocated type.

Chapter 10

MENTAL RETARDATION

Many parents of mentally retarded children have gone from one physician to another and have been told that their child "would grow out of it," that "children have different rates of development—don't be concerned," and so on. The doctor knows that this is not so, but he thinks that he is doing the parents a kindness by letting them continue to hope that their child is not retarded. Fortunately, the properly trained physician knows that the parents of the retarded child must eventually accept the facts in the case. The earlier a direct evaluation of the situation is provided, the better it will be for all those concerned. The physician should provide understanding for the parents gradually and with the greatest compassion because there is no more prolonged anguish than that produced by a retarded child. Nonetheless, the parents will learn eventually that the child is retarded, and their adjustment is easier if they learn it early. On the other hand, the physician must be sure of his diagnosis and not plague the parents with dire speculations.

It is certainly not easy to have a retarded child in the family. It need not all be a grim experience, and it is a rigorous test of one's character. Fortunate are the parents who have a sense of humor because it can change a situation from one that is awful to one that is awfully funny. The poem below was written by Lucy Cook, a member of our local Association for Retarded Children. Small children, retarded or not, can cause things to get pretty hectic around the house, and many mothers have found that merely thinking of this poem makes them smile again.

"THE WAY OF THE WORLD"

Pans are to bang on,
String is to eat.
Chairs are for bouncing,
Windows to beat.

Dogs are to kiss, and
Squash is to spit.
Laps are to climb on,
Cousins to hit.

Drawers are to empty.
Dolls are to throw.
Hair is for pulling.
Cars are to go.

And it's strange that nobody
At all understands
That the gleaming toilet is
For washing your hands.

This chapter is concerned with all those deviations from normal intelligence that were known in the past as feeble-mindedness and then as mental deficiency and are now known as mental retardation. The feeble-minded are deficient because they have a retarded mental growth rate. Whatever we call it, it is one of our extremely frustrating mental health problems because most of the mentally retarded do not recover from their disease, nor do they usually die young.

The most difficult fact to accept, after that of the retardation itself, is that it may be genetic. The reason that the parents of the retarded find genetics threatening to them is that they think of heredity and mental retardation in terms of gruesome families of the Jukes and Kallikak type. Unfortunately, such families exist today, and it is probable that some proportion of their troubles have a genetic basis. However, these socially degenerate families are at one extreme of the types of mental retardation, and there is no reason whatever why most parents of mentally retarded children should erroneously identify with such social problem families.

The old axiom that we are the product of *both* our heredity and our environment is just as true for mental traits as for physical characteristics. The problem always consists of trying to determine the influence of the individual factors involved, with less concern for whether they happen to be genetic or not.

In order to get a general idea of the roles of heredity and environment for a small collection of various types of mental deficiencies, we can look at the comparisons between identical (one-egg) and fraternal (two-egg) twins. Böök (1953) includes the data of two authors, Smith and Juda, and these are combined in Table VIII. The high percentage of concordance between the identical twins and the much lower agreement between the fraternal twins is good evidence of a strong genetic basis for many of the cases of mental retardation. It should be remembered that fraternal twins are definitely full siblings and that much of the concordance that is shown by them will also have a genetic basis often of the simple mendelian recessive type.

TABLE VIII   The Striking Concordance, or Agreement, of Identical Twins with Mental Retardation Compared with the Lack of Agreement among Fraternal Twins

	Both Mentally Retarded	One Mentally Retarded
Identical	74 (97%)	2
Fraternal	80 (37%)	138

One of the most useful techniques for the geneticist is the observation of the results of consanguineous unions. We know that if a specific type of mental retardation depends upon a simple *rare* recessive gene in the homozygous condition for its expression, we will find a higher consanguinity rate among the parents of the retarded children than in a control series. Increased consanguinity rates are found for rare types of mental retardation and if they are not present, this indicates clearly that there is some other basis for the rare type of retardation than one pair of recessive genes.

An elegant illustration of the leverage offered by the consanguinity tool has been reported by Aronson and Volk (1962). They confirmed what has been known for a long time, that pedigrees of infantile amaurotic idiocy from Jewish families show a higher rate of consanguinity than the parentage of normal children. The disease is even more rare in non-Jewish families, and here the affected children have consanguineous parentage in at least 30 per cent of the cases. Furthermore, the ancestry of many New York Jewish patients can be traced back to one small area of northeastern Poland and southern Lithuania. Thus, confirmation of the mendelian recessive basis for infantile amaurotic idiocy comes about by independent chains of evidence, leaving no doubt of the importance of genetics in the etiology of this specific type of retardation.

The study of family pedigrees is an obvious and essential step in judging whether a trait depends to any large degree upon genetic factors, and if so, what the mendelian mechanism may be.

It is impossible here to take up the many different types of mental retardation. They are grossly different in their behavior and depend upon different genes for their occurrence. Most of them have neither medical names nor descriptions as yet. Many of them probably represent the segregation into one person of several different pairs of genes, each of which merely lowers intelligence a little. Such persons make up the lower part of the normal curve for intelligence. The very large families in which many relatives have mental retardation probably result from assortive or preferential mating of people with multiple genes for low intelligence, as shown by Reed, Reed and Palm (1954). Furthermore, many cases are purely environmental in origin, though not as many as sometimes alleged. Obstetricians should resent the rather common insinuation that each time a child is found to be mentally retarded the retardation must be due to birth injuries.

The physician should consult a medical geneticist for counseling regarding specific types of mental deficiency, as the subject is highly complicated and specialized. However, the writer would like to present some general considerations concerning the general problem of mental deficiency.

The common, garden variety of moron family without cultural motivations is not likely to come to anyone for counseling about the rampant mental retardation in the family. The family in which the young couple is of reasonable intelligence but has produced a retarded child or has mentally retarded close relatives is more likely to come to the physician for various kinds of information. This latter type of family can be helped more, as the members will be able to comprehend something of the significance of heredity or of the environmental factors responsible for the retarded condition.

Naturally, the first problem for the physician will be that of diagnosing, if possible, the type of mental retardation involved. If it is clear that the retardation is purely of environmental origin, the situation is relatively simple, because the environmental factors may be replaced by favorable ones in some cases. If the mental retardation results from some previously described recessive condition, such as infantile amaurotic idiocy, the couple has to be advised that there is a one in four chance of a repetition of their misfortune. Usually the condition will be an undifferentiated one, which has gradually become apparent to the parents but which they have not really accepted because of the lack of physical signs accompanying the gradual retardation. Consequently, the parents must be informed in a sympathetic fashion that their child may be expected to drop farther behind his contemporaries each year. To deliberately shoot the bull, pass the buck, and send the parents to seven different doctors just isn't cricket.

The reason that prompt action is necessary with mental deficiency is that the other children in the family are concerned with the situation. The mentally retarded child will need, and will usually get much more than a fair share of the attention and resources of the parents. A drooling idiot in the family is a source of embarrassment to its sibs and will cause them to go elsewhere for social contacts. The retarded child is an invitation to improper sexual exploitation by ill-mannered neighbors or others.

Very frequently it will be the duty of the physician to convince the parents that the child would be better off in the state school than at home and to help with the procedures necessary to have the child admitted to the public institution. Even though the building may be old and crowded and the food scorned by Duncan Hines, the child will find himself among his equals and he will be able to compete with them, whereas in the home community he will be always either overprotected or cruelly rejected from social contacts. Children are more interested in satisfactory contacts with other children than they are in culinary fine points or the design of their bedspreads. Actually, many state institutions are much more elegant than the homes from which some of the patients come. To be sure, it is a little hard on the vanity of the parents to find that after a week or two their small retarded child no longer misses them, but it is fortunate that this does happen. There is now a National Association of the Parents of Retarded Children, which can be of great help to parents who are faced with the difficult decision concerning institutionalization of their child.

The physician may object that none of this is his business and that it is the responsibility of the social worker. But it *is* his business. Mental retardation is one of the most serious and important disease conditions, and the physician is obligated to help the parents in a positive and vigorous fashion. The physician is not paid just to prescribe pills; most druggists could do that, if the law allowed it. The physician has a higher duty.

A side issue is whether families in which a retarded child has occurred, and in which a decision to have no more children has been made, should adopt children. Most reputable agencies will not place a child in a family where the retarded member is still present. If the parents will institutionalize the retarded child, they may be considered as prospective foster parents. Because of the shortage of newborn babies to be placed, the applicants still are not likely to have their needs filled. There are many very desirable older children, as well as babies with a trace of Oriental or African blood, available for adoption. The physician should urge that these be accepted if the parents are not prejudiced.

The physician is inclined to think, in cases of sterility of one member of the couple or in cases where the genetic risk is great and adoption seems advisable, that once he has suggested the idea of adoption and the couple accept it, the problem is solved. It would be wonderful if the solution were so simple. Actually, little progress will have been made. There just are not enough children available to meet the adoption needs. There are probably about 50 couples wanting children for adoption to each available child. The agencies do not have this many on their waiting lists, however, for the simple reasons that after they have failed to supply a couple on the list for some months or years, they merely scratch the name off the list, notifying the couple that not enough babies were available to begin to meet the demand.

Childless couples often find themselves in an almost unbearable position. Their desire for children has become magnified out of reasonable proportions. Consequently, they are willing to resort to almost anything to obtain a family of healthy children. Since the discovery of the technique of donor insemination, semiadoption has been used on a wide scale to provide children where the husband is sterile or the couple have found themselves to be heterozygous for some serious genetic recessive, such as that for infantile amaurotic idiocy.

An excellent paper by Rutherford and Banks (1954), two Seattle physicians, gives some very enlightening case histories of couples who had utilized semiadoption to the benefit of all concerned. It also points out the tendency of couples who suspect that one member or the other is sterile to determine which one is barren by calculated adultery of the traditional type. The fertility clinic can be of great service in preventing tragic experiments of this latter sort. A follow-up study by Farris and Garrison (1954) showed that for 38 couples who had achieved a child by donor insemination all comments were favorable and all spouses desired a second child by the same method.

There is also the problem of the ordinary adoption of children one or both of whose parents are mentally deficient. The physician will be asked for an opinion whether the child is expected to have normal or retarded mental development. Naturally, few persons would care to adopt a child if there is an appreciable chance of his being mentally retarded. Largely because of a superficial interpretation by others of the work of

Skodak and Skeels (1949), the myth has been generated that adoption in itself is certain to improve the I.Q. values of the children. This may be true, though actually there is little evidence for it. In the above study there were 11 mothers who were mentally retarded, with an average I.Q. of 63. Their 11 children who were placed for adoption scored an average I.Q. of 94, a remarkable gain of 31 points. However, we know from Galton's law of filial regression toward the mean that the children would have averaged higher than their true mothers even if they had remained with them instead of being placed. Consequently, there is no way of evaluating what proportion of the gain could be attributed to the better environments of the adoptive parents.

At first glance, the above gain of 31 points to give an average I.Q. of 94 for the 11 children of the mentally retarded mothers looks pretty good. However, the foster parents are not adopting an average but instead, a single child. The bottom 3 of the 11 children had I.Q.'s of 66, 74 and 87, respectively. These 3 children compose one-quarter of those from the retarded mothers and would seem to have dubious possibilities of satisfactory adjustment in the adoptive families. Most agencies would not place children with I.Q. values below 75. The difficult question is whether the whole group of children from mentally retarded mothers should be denied placement until old enough to get reliable intelligence tests just to protect one-fourth of the adoptive parents from getting children who will be mentally retarded. The answer to the question will have to be produced by each agency and will vary, no doubt, from place to place.

The mental deficiencies and the mental illnesses are our all-important health problems, and much more attention and money must be devoted to all aspects of these problems. A survey of research in the field of mental subnormality is given in a book by Masland, Sarason and Gladwin (1958), which is recommended as a basis for extensive study of this area of work.

ILLUSTRATIVE EXAMPLES

1. *Request.*
   A county welfare board has an illegitimate boy in its custody, whose mother is a mentally retarded cretin. The mother actually graduated from a large high school, ranking 230 in a class of 254, but never did passing work. She had little idea of what any subject was about but always tried very hard. She was very unhappy, completely lacking in social graces, and was avoided by the other students. At three months of age, she was put on thyroid, which she still takes daily. She is large-boned and well-developed physically, though odd in appearance.

   Her baby seemed normal at birth and continued to be so at subsequent examinations. He is now six months of age. It is thought that the boy should be placed for adoption, unless there are indications to the contrary. What is your recommendation?

   Reply.
   There is no general agreement whether cretinism is hereditary or not. However, it is a clearly delimited glandular dysfunction and could well depend upon some complicated type of recessive heredity.

   From the practical point of view, let us assume that cretinism does depend upon recessive heredity for its appearance. The chances that the father of the baby carried recessive heredity for cretinism are very small, as the disease is rare and the father was not related to the boy's mother. Therefore, the child may be expected to continue his normal development and to have normal children. As far as can be seen, the environment of all members of the family has been excellent. The mother's brother has an I.Q. of 121 and is extremely well thought of in the community. We recommend that the baby be placed for adoption at once. The boy may carry recessive heredity for cretinism, but as all of us carry some undesirable recessive genes we cannot discriminate against this particular boy.

   Follow-up.
   The baby was placed for adoption. He is now three years old and is as fine a boy as one could find. The foster parents are delighted with him and are pleased with his excellent mental and physical development.

2. *Request.*
   A pair of identical girl twins were born out of wedlock to a mother with an I.Q. of 70. The mother completed the sixth grade, leaving when she became 16. She is a stutterer. The maternal grand-

mother maintains that she completed the fifth grade, but that is questionable. Her I.Q. is 48. The maternal grandfather had no formal education and was a shoemaker. One maternal aunt had an I.Q. of 51. Three maternal uncles were of limited mental capacity but completed grade school. The remaining maternal aunt had an I.Q. of 121. She left the home community and went to Minneapolis, where she completed high school. She has an excellent reputation, quite different from the community opinion of her brothers and sisters.

The twin girls are nine years old and have been living with their mother and grandmother. Their paternity was never established. One twin has an I.Q. of 127 and the other an I.Q. of 131. Both twins are very superior in memory span for all kinds of material, in ability to generalize and see similarities, and in ability to comprehend absurdities. They both were only average in solving problems of fact involving social comprehension; this may be due in part to the wretched and impoverished environment in which they were reared. Both have the ability to do excellent college work when they reach that level. Their vocabularies are above average but not superior.

We (a church adoption agency) have been asked to make an adoptive home placement for these nine year old twins and wonder what prediction one can make for the future. We are especially interested in whether any recommendation can be made as to children born to these girls assuming that the men they marry are of average and normal intelligence. What are the possibilities of a reverting back to the low mental capacity of the twins' mother and grandmother?

Reply.
Your primary concern should be with the intellectual future of the twins. It is quite clear that they are capable of college work, and their talents in this direction are somewhat better than average parents should expect to find in their own children.

The study of Terman on gifted children showed that one generation later in their progeny there were a few reversions back to low mental capacity. The production of mentally retarded children by highly intelligent parents is an established fact and an ever-present source of concern. However, the adoption service cannot be expected to guarantee the excellence of subsequent generations born to the children it places. It can be satisfied if these children make satisfactory adjustments with the foster parents while associated with them.

3.   *Request.*
Mr. C. has spoken to me about institutionalizing his daughter through probate court proceedings. The daughter has congenital absence of her right eye. The child has an I.Q. of probably less than 50.

Since I will probably be one of the doctors called upon when the
probate court proceedings take place, I would appreciate a note from
you advising me of your opinion in such a case.

Reply.
From this distance it appears that the little girl has congenital
micropthalmos (or anophthalmos) with accompanying mental deficiency. A monograph on this subject was published in *Acta Psychiatrica
et Neurologica* in 1949 by Sjögren and Larsson. The microphthalmic
child is not always mentally deficient, though the prognosis is poor.

The advantages to the child and her family that could come
from institutionalization are many. (1) The staff is able to train the
child to a greater degree of proficiency than the parents, who have
had no previous experience with this problem. (2) The child will be
with other children of similar age and capacity and will not be subject to the insults of normal children. (3) If the child stays at home
it will receive more than its share of attention from the parents, to the
detriment of the normal sibs. (4) At the institution the future of the
child is secure, whereas at home the death of the parents would leave
the child in a helpless position. (5) The Division of Public Institutions
can be of help to the family and child as soon as it receives guardianship of the child, regardless of whether or not institutionalization
actually takes place.

Follow-up.
The child is now under the guardianship of the state. The
parents adopted a child and did not intend to risk the repetition of
their previous misfortune. They did, however, have one more child,
a normal boy.

Second Follow-up.
Just as the first edition of this book was released, this case re-
opened in a most amazing way. The girl was institutionalized and still
did not talk at age six. At this time in another family a girl was born
with congenital absence of the right eye. The two families were un-
aware of each other at the time and lived in different towns, but it
was found that the two girls with identical defects were third cousins.
The mothers of the two girls are second cousins. Are the two fathers,
who are definitely genetically unrelated to each other and to their
wives, both carriers of an autosomal recessive for the trait, or is there
a dominant gene with very poor penetrance responsible for such exact
duplication of this characteristic?

The second affected child was operated upon for intended cos-
metic improvement, but it died. The parents of the first child have
been very active in the Minnesota Association for Retarded Children,

and I have seen them many times during these activities. I know that they have made important contributions to many parents who have had the problem of accepting mental retardation in their child, and then of accepting a genetic basis for it, as must be done in many cases.

Chapter 11

THE CENTRAL NERVOUS
SYSTEM SYNDROME

In Minnesota between 10 and 20 per cent of all deaths of infants under one year of age are due to congenital malformations. These malformations are of interest to the geneticist, as he is justified in expecting that many of them depend upon relatively strong hereditary forces. The brilliant victories over bacterial and viral causes of death in the first year of life are one of the milestones in the progress of civilization. There are still many antibiotic problems demanding attention, but, in general, one might expect some shift in emphasis from the micro-organisms to the genes in the future.

Fewer victories have been gained in the struggle with congenital malformations, as the answers are more elusive. This is particularly true of the three nervous system malformations to be considered in this chapter: anencephaly, hydrocephaly and spina bifida. The definitions of these three abnormalities seem to overlap, and it is sometimes difficult to separate them. This difficulty is not evidence in itself that the three are genetically related, but it will be shown that they probably are.

According to Murphy (1947), about 60 per cent of the deaths and stillbirths due to congenital malformations were the result of abnormalities of the nervous system. Record and McKeown (1949, 1950 and 1956) have studied the complete sample of deaths and stillbirths from 1940 through 1947 in Birmingham, England. The 930 deaths in 158,307 births (0.59 per cent) due to nervous system defects are shown in Table IX. These studies understate the actual frequency of nervous system defects as they are derived from death certificates. A fair percentage of cases of hydrocephaly and spina bifida is missed because the children survive infancy; anencephalics born before the 28th week of gestation will also be missing.

Record (1961) studied the Scottish statistics for anencephaly and found that, while the stillbirth rate 1956–58 was only about half what it was in 1938–41, the contribution of anencephalus alone to the stillbirth rate increased from 5.8 per cent in the earlier years to 12.7 per cent. Improved environmental conditions did not result in a decrease of anencephaly; instead, there seems to have been an increase from 2.39 anencephalics per 1,000 total births to 2.99 per 1,000. This does not mean that there are no environmental relationships. In the same paper it is shown that the incidence varies both with parity and with age of the mother. Anencephaly has a high incidence among the first-born, especially when the mother is very young, and among the higher birth ranks, especially when the mother is old. The incidence fluctuates with the season of the year from a low

TABLE IX   Distribution of the Main Types of Nervous System Defects

	Stillbirths	Neonatal	Later Infancy	Total	Per Cent
Spina bifida	120	202	67	389	42
Anencephaly	347	19	—	366	39
Hydrocephaly	112	24	14	150	16
Others	5	15	5	25	3
Total	584	260	86	930	
Per cent	63	28	9		100

of 2.39 in a March–May trimester to a high of 3.18 in December–February.

Record ruled out influenza, rubella and most of the usual infections as primary causes of anencephalus. However, he pointed out that the striking correlation between lower social class and higher incidence shown by Edwards (1958), along with the seasonal fluctuation, is consistent with a primary effect by an unknown infective agent. Such correlations are leads for future research but are not proof of anything until the infective agent is identified. This search will be difficult, as anencephaly is laid down about three weeks after conception.

Hydrocephaly and spina bifida seem to be correlated with social class and the other environmental variables in much the same way as anencephaly. If anencephaly and hydrocephaly are associated with spina bifida more frequently than one would expect due to coincidence, one can assume some common factor or factors in the etiology of all three. There is a remarkable excess of combinations of both types, which implies that the three defects have the same etiology in many cases. Probably the same genetic background as well as similar environmental factors are responsible for their appearance. Record and McKeown's calculations are given in Table X. We are therefore justified in consider-

TABLE X   The Large Excess of Combinations of the Three Defects of the Nervous System Observed Compared with the Expectations for These Combinations Due to Coincidence

	Number of Combinations Expected	Number of Combinations Observed
Anencephaly with spina bifida	0.98	34
Hydrocephaly with spina bifida	0.75	129

ing that most cases of these three defects belong to the central nervous system category.

It is necessary to study a series of control families in order to determine whether a trait is "familial" or not. Record and McKeown, in their classic papers already cited, studied the families of 742 dead defectives and the families of 742 normal controls. They found that there had been 6.5 times as many nervous system defects among the siblings of the dead malformed as among the sibs of the controls. These neat data are shown in Table XI. A similar excess among relatives other than sibs was found also, although not as great a one, as would be expected because of the more remote relationship. The familial nature of this syndrome is therefore firmly established.

The low frequency (1.89 per cent) of nervous system malformations among the sibs of the affected propositi would seem to indicate only some sort of weak hereditary background, as it is far below the 25 per cent expected for a "good" recessive gene. However, it is likely that the 1.89 per cent represents only a small part of the embryos that have nervous system malformations. Record and McKeown show a significant excess of abortions and stillbirths among the sibs of the propositi compared with that among the sibs of the controls. A summary of their material is reproduced in Table XII.

TABLE XI   The Excess of Nervous System Defects in the Sibs of the Defective Propositi Compared with Those in the Sibs of the Normal Controls

	Total Number of Offspring	Fraternities	Sibs	Defects among Sibs	Per Cent
Malformation series	2,276	742	1,534	29	1.89
Control series	2,117	742	1,375	4	0.29
Percentage of defects in the Birmingham births............................					0.59

TABLE XII   The Excess of Abortions and Stillbirths among the Sibs of Propositi and Controls

	Sibs of Each Type of Malformation					
	1. Anen- cephaly	2. Spina Bifida	3. Hydro- cephaly	Average (1–3) (a)	Average Controls (b)	Difference (a–b)
Stillbirth rate per 1,000 births	52.2	21.8	89.5	45.1	22.9	22.2 ± 6.8
Abortion rate per 1,000 known conceptions	116.7	107.1	98.2	109.8	74.6	35.2 ± 10.3
Total stillbirth and abortion rate for 1,000 known conceptions	210.4	178.0	221.1	198.3	148.5	49.8 ± 13.6

It is reasonable to assume that many embryos that die because of these abnormalities are expelled at such early stages that they are not recognized as abortions. As it is, Table XII shows 49.8 per 1,000 more known conceptions to end in still-births and abortions in the families with the defective children than in the families of the controls. It seems legitimate to add this excess (4.98 per cent) to the 1.89 per cent, which gives roughly 7 per cent lethal conceptions that should be most reasonably considered to result from these nervous system abnormalities.

In a smaller but very careful study, Böök and Rayner (1950) restricted their consideration to anencephaly. In 42 families with anencephalic propositi the sibs consisted of 86 children born alive and normal, 1 stillborn of unknown cause, 1 with spina bifida and 22 spontaneous abortions. Thus, at least 24 out of 110 conceptions (22 per cent) of sibs were not normal. If we subtract the 14.8 per cent of lethal conceptions found by Record and McKeown in their control families, we get 7 per cent excess abnormalities for the Swedish data. The English and Swedish data are in agreement that there is at least a 7 per cent excess of abnormal conceptions in addition to the propositi in their families compared with the control families. It would be interesting to know just what proportion of abortions are due to these frequent defects of the nervous system. It must be large.

Regardless of the hereditary background involved, we can give genetic counseling, particularly since the publication of the fine studies of Record and McKeown. They point out that in practice the doctor is required to comment on the likelihood of recurrence after a malformed baby has been born.

There were 470 sibs born after the first malformed infant in their (1950b) study of which 13, or 2.8 per cent, had nervous system defects. The expected incidence, were there no hereditary influence, was found to be 0.45 per cent. MacMahon, Pugh and Ingalls (1953) in a study of Rhode Island maternity hospital material found 18 affected with central nervous system defects out of a total of 339 births, or 5.3 per cent, subsequent to the birth of an affected individual. The observed incidence is approximately six times the expected. The observed from the combined studies is 3.4 per cent. The chance that a mother will produce a second abnormal child at her next parturition is better than 3 per cent. But the chance that the next conception will result in a malformed child *or* an abortion is close to 25 per cent. Böök and Rayner (1950) give a comparable estimate of over 20 per cent for anencephalics and abortions together.

The study of Penrose (1946) showed 7 subsequent malformations, 7 stillbirths and 19 abortions among 200 conceptions subsequent to that of the propositus. These 33 abnormal conceptions account for 16 per cent of those following that of the propositus.

Fraser Roberts (1962) carried out the heroic task of finding the risk of recurrence of anencephaly or spina bifida for families that already had two affected children. He found 53 children born subsequent to the second affected child, and 8 of them displayed the central nervous system syndrome. This is 1 in 7, or from 10 to 15 per cent risk. I have had about 10 counseling cases of women who had two affected children, and one of these has produced a third anencephalic child. All three anencephalics were strikingly similar in that they survived for about three months with the aid of oxygen administration. This similarity would lead one to expect that a simple mendelian recessive gene for anencephaly is present in this particular family.

One might point out that the risk of an abortion in the normal control families is also unfortunately high. This will be small comfort to the mother who has produced her second malformed child or has had an abortion after having been assured by a kind physician that the chance of such a thing happening was negligible, no greater than for any other woman.

The data given above, elegant as they are, do not help a great deal in counseling a young man who underwent surgery for spina bifida when a baby and now wishes to marry and have a family. Nor have we considered the status of the vast number of cases of spina bifida occulta. Sutow and Pryde (1956) found that 95 (58.3 per cent) of 163 Japanese children had spina bifida occulta involving the fifth lumbar and/or the first sacral vertebra. They thought that fusion continues after birth to perhaps seven years of age. They suggested the very reasonable hypothesis that it is a simple retardation in development.

There is the possibility that spina bifida occulta is the heterozygous condition that, when homozygous, results in spina bifida aperta and the other manifestations of the central nervous system syndrome. The relatively high incidence of this syndrome in the population implies that if any gene concerned must be present in the homozygous condition in order to cause severe damage, then the carrier frequency would be somewhere in the neighborhood of the incidence of spina bifida occulta in the Japanese children, although certainly not that high.

Edwards (1961), in his search for environmental factors involved in the central nervous system syndrome, found a few families in which hydrocephalus behaved as a strictly sex-linked trait. One individual family pedigree displayed 15 affected males. The anomalies shown in these families are not typical of the mass of cases with the central nervous system syndrome, and they indicate the heterogeneity one should expect with the common malformations.

Regardless of whether one's bias is toward environmental or genetic factors as the etiologic agents, and realizing that different factors may be responsible in different affected individuals effective counseling may be given. All persons who have come to me for information regarding this syndrome have considered their risks to be much greater than warranted according to any relevant theory of the etiology of the central nervous system malformations.

In summary, regardless of whether genetic or environmental factors are primarily responsible for these anomalies, there is an average chance for a repetition of one or more of them in subsequent pregnancies. Fortunately, the chance of producing a living child with some aspect of the central nervous system syndrome is only about 3 per cent, and most couples are willing to take this relatively small risk. They should be instructed as to the magnitude of this risk, even though it is small. The chance of having a miscarriage or stillbirth at each subsequent pregnancy may approach 25 per cent, but this misfortune is less traumatic in the long run than the birth of a viable child with hydrocephalus or spina bifida.

It comes as a shock to realize that more conceptions are lost because of these three nervous system abnormalities than, for example, because of erythroblastosis. The need for research in the field of congenital nervous system abnormalities is acute, even though at the moment the prospects of preventive measures are small.

ILLUSTRATIVE EXAMPLES

1. *Request.*
    The writer often gives talks on human heredity to the obstetric staffs of various hospitals. At one of them, a staff member asked about a patient who had two normal stepchildren but had lost both her own children due to spina bifida. One died at birth and the other at about two years of age. He was given the risk figures. The next day he phoned and asked whether the writer would see the patient. He agreed to do so, although he thought the physician could do a better job with her, now that he knew the risks involved for subsequent pregnancies.

    Mrs. G. appeared and stated flatly that she was not interested in taking any risk at all. It turned out that the obstetrician was Catholic, but she was Protestant; apparently he had sent her to the Dight Insitute with the expectation that birth control information would be provided for her.

Reply.
    After it became clear that she was not interested in genetics, it was suggested that she see a different physician for contraceptive advice, although no particular one was recommended.

First Follow-up.
    A phone call from a different obstetrician stated that Mrs. G. had carelessly left her contraceptive appliance in the bureau drawer too often and was now pregnant. She was in a bad mental state, insisting upon a therapeutic abortion. He was prepared to oblige and asked for the writer's opinion. The writer did not think that the rather small risk involved justified the destruction of the embryo.

Second Follow-up.
    A phone call to the second obstetrician a year later revealed that they had taken the counselor's advice and that a normal child had been born. The physician was extremely grateful that he had accepted the counseling and said that Mrs. G. was now in excellent mental and physical health.

2.   One of the discouraging aspects of present-day medical practice is the usually incorrect and cavalier fashion in which medical "informants" answer the questions that come to the press. The following is an example of this in the local press.

Question.
     When a baby is born with a "water head," what is the cause of it and is it inherited?

Answer.
     There is no known cause. This is a developmental defect. It is not hereditary.—Medical Informant.

3.   Most couples usually come to the Dight Institute only once. They learn that the chances of a repetition of their genetic problem are less than they had expected. They go home and have subsequent normal children and may even forget that they have been at the Dight Institute. Not all cases end so happily, however. The following situation resulted in four visits to the Dight Institute. We hope that no more visits will be necessary. A summary of the reproductive history is the only way to encompass this long story within a reasonable space.

     The husband has a harelip. The first pregnancy ended at seven months with a placenta previa and the child died; it had a harelip. The parents were quite upset and concerned about the possibility of a repetition of the harelip. The second and third pregnancies were normal, and everything seemed fine. The fourth pregnancy resulted in a hydrocephalic child. The mother stated that she had the "flu" all during this pregnancy. This remark was factually correct but genetically misleading, as will be seen shortly. However, in spite of the hope that the hydrocephaly was caused by influenza and not by genetic factors, the couple had their obstetrician try artificial insemination twice but without success. They then adopted a child.

     This couple is near the top of the economic heap where numerous active, healthy children are a status symbol. They came for counseling with the hope that they might have one more healthy child of their own. They were encouraged by the fact that central nervous system defects were only expected in a small fraction of any living offspring that they might have. Unfortunately, the fifth pregnancy reresulted in an anencephalic child. This experience left them greatly disappointed but not bitter, and they spoke of the possibility of trying adoption or artificial insemination again.

     The story did not end there. The couple adopted a child. They now had two normal girls of their own and two adopted boys. Three years later they tried once more for a normal child but once again were greatly disappointed at the birth of an anencephalic child, which died in a few hours. They are now very proud of the children they have and are willing to concentrate their efforts on them. It is hard for them to believe that they could have a normal child again, after three central nervous system failures in a row. This compounding of misfortunes is too strong a force to be overcome by even the most cheerful statistics.

Chapter 12

"CURES" FOR GENETIC DISEASES

(Phenylketonuria, Fibrocystic Disease and Diabetes)

The cult of ancestor worship has always flourished throughout the world. We point with pride to our Mayflower ancestors, even though our actual genetic relationship to each of them is almost nonexistent. On the other hand, any genetic disease in the family may be quite threatening because a person may not wish to identify with the affected relative and because many genetic diseases are incurable. However, "cures" are being found for genetic diseases, and every time a new cure is found some of the harmful effects of another gene are overruled by modern medicine.

No genetic disease is ever cured in the strictest sense, because the gene itself has not been affected and in the cured person it has a better chance than before to be transmitted to subsequent generations. The cures are palliatives, which permit the person with the unwanted genes to overrule his own genetics by medical means and thus function as a practically normal person. Most genetic cures, such as insulin, do not restore the functions of the individual to complete normality, but the improvement is usually close to miraculous and is highly recommended. The fact that each medical triumph over genetic diseases is dysgenic, in that it increases the frequency of the unwanted gene in subsequent generations, should not prevent its use, but it does bring up the problem of the responsibility of the "cured" person for the increased reproduction that the cure permits.

In this chapter and in Chapters 13 and 14, there will be brief considerations of several diseases with varying degrees of genetic influence in their etiology for which cures have been found. Some of these are rare and would not be considered, other than in the Appendix, were it not for the fact that because of the excitement aroused by the cures, there is a great deal of counseling activity.

Phenylketonuria (P.K.U.)

This disease is rare, with a frequency somewhere between 1 case in 10 to 20 thousand births. The cases may be detected by the third month of life by the diaper test, which consists of placing a few drops of 10 per cent ferric chloride on a wet diaper. The appearance of a green color indicates the presence of phenylpyruvic acid in the urine; if the diaper test continues to be positive, the pediatrician should have tests made to determine the phenylalanine level of the blood. Pheni-stix may be obtained from the Ames Company, Elkhart, Indiana, and used to detect phenylpyruvic acid in the urine.

Guthrie (1961) has developed a most ingenious assay method, using *Bacillus subtilis*, which should permit the detection of phenylketonuria in babies before they leave the hospital. The urgency for early detection of the affected child stems from the fact that the mental retardation associated with excess phenylalanine in the blood can be prevented, at least to a significant degree, if a corrective diet is instituted promptly. For a discussion of the dietary treatment of phenylketonuria, see Woolf,

Griffiths, Moncrieff, Coates and Dillistone (1958). These workers think that the mental retardation found in the persons with this disease results from phenylalanine intoxication.

It is clear that the basic etiology of the disease depends upon the presence in the homozygous condition of a gene for absence of phenylalanine hydroxylase in the liver. It takes two doses of the defective gene to produce symptoms of the disease. However, in some cases the carrier of one dose of the gene may be distinguished from normal persons who are not carriers. Normal persons can be tested for heterozygosity by having them drink a phenylalanine "cocktail"; their plasma phenylalanine level is determined in relation to the level just before the "cocktail" was taken. There is, unfortunately, some overlapping of the phenylalanine tolerance of normals and carrier normals even when the discriminant scores of Wang, Morton and Waisman (1960) are used. Nonetheless, some individuals can be tagged as carriers and others as noncarriers, which has great value for counseling purposes.

There is a recent account by Fujiki, Drew, Miyake, Nemoto, Sujaku and Skimada (1961) of a retarded man with P.K.U. who produced a daughter with the disease. This man had not received the dietary treatment, but his reproduction, and that of two similar cases, indicates that those children whose intelligence has been preserved by the prophylactic diet will reproduce in many cases, thus increasing the frequency of a clearly undesirable gene. The most important counseling problem will be that of trying to educate affected individuals so that they will not wish to marry another affected person or a carrier. In the first instance, 100 per cent of the children would be affected and in the second case, 50 per cent. No couple has the right to produce a child with a 100 per cent chance of having P.K.U., and it is doubtful whether a couple has the right deliberately to take a 50 per cent chance of producing such a serious defect.

It is possible to debate the question of the rights of parents to take large deliberate risks of producing children with gross defects. Everyone would agree that once an abnormal child is born, it should be salvaged whenever possible. In order to salvage the child with P.K.U., the test must be carried out during the first few weeks of life. It is extraordinarily simple to drop some 10 per cent ferric chloride on a wet diaper. There is still considerable resistance among physicians to doing this on the grounds that it is a lot of wasted effort, as one might not find an affected child in years. This is true, but is it ethical to condemn a child to a lifetime of mental retardation merely to save a little trouble? We have succeeded in getting the well baby clinics of the Twin Cities to make the ferric chloride test a routine part of the checkup, and to our surprise three cases have been found in about 10,000 babies. This rate must be too high, but the investment in effort has paid off handsomely. Furthermore, there isn't any religious group that could object to dropping ferric chloride on a child's diaper. Finally, the frequency of P.K.U. is greater than that of a smallpox, for which vaccination is routine.

Fibrocystic Disease (Mucoviscidosis)

This disease is of great interest because in the past it was almost always lethal. It is dependent upon the homozygous condition of a recessive gene for its expression. Affected babies can now be salvaged by the use of antibiotics in conjunction with pancreatin and special diets. There is no problem of mental deficiency here, and reproduction should not be upset by the disease. There should soon be data on the children of patients with fibrocystic disease, as their life expectancy has been increased very significantly. Schwachman and Kulczycki (1958) reported on 105 cases observed for 5 to 14 years. Only 10 of the 105 patients died during that time. This presents more of a eugenics problem because the disease has a higher incidence than P.K.U. Consequently, the carrier state will be more frequent than it is for P.K.U., and there will be a much greater chance that the fibrocystic patient will marry a carrier and have 50 per cent of his children affected.

Steinberg and Brown (1960) found an incidence of 1 fibrocystic birth in 3,700 in Ohio—the best estimate there is. According to this statistic, 1 in every 33 persons is heterozygous for the gene. Therefore, 1 in every 33 patients who survives and marries could expect to produce a child with fibrocystic disease if he had any appreciable number of children because if he does marry a carrier, the chance of an affected child is 50 per cent for each birth. Consequently, it becomes increasingly desirable to be able to detect the carriers of this gene. There is hope that refinements of the sweat test will permit this determination with reliability. Dr. Paul di Sant'-Agnese has developed a sweat-test program that rests upon the discovery that patients with cystic fibrosis excrete up to 10 times as much salt as normal persons in their sweat. Apparently the normal carriers excrete more chloride than the normals who are free of the gene in many cases, as shown graphically by Smoller and Hsia (1959). Unfortunately, the technique still needs refinement and only those heterozygotes with high values can be definitely tagged as carriers; a low value does not guarantee freedom from the gene.

The genes for fibrocystic disease present in the population represent mutations at different points in time and doubtless represent different chemical changes. It is entirely reasonable to expect to find an occasional family in which the gene behaves as a dominant. A single dose of such a dominant gene might be expected to cause less severe symptoms than the double dose. This situation might account for the interesting observations of Karlish and Tarnoky (1960), who found that 11 out of 33 adults and 1 of 15 children attending a chest clinic for bronchitis, emphysema, asthma or bronchiectasis had abnormally high sweat-electrolyte levels consistent with mucoviscidosis. It is not possible to describe techniques in this book, but for readers interested in the sweat-electrolyte measurements and other references, the article by Gibson and Cooke (1959) is recommended.

In summary, it should be clear that fibrocystic disease presents a critical genetic counseling situation. Not only are the chances of a repetition of the disease 25 per cent for each child of carrier parents, but the cost is high when the gamble is lost. There is still a large chance that the child will die, usually after a long period of intermittent hospitalization. The financial cost can easily exceed an average of $200 per month, which for more than one child at a time may exceed the monthly wages of the parents. With such a serious problem it would be unrealistic to avoid the question of future limitation of the family size. All religions would permit complete limitation, and the most conservative ones would prescribe the rhythm method or complete abstinence. This prescription is easy to obtain but difficult to observe, as any well-adjusted married couple knows.

Diabetes Mellitus

The general public assumes that the discovery of insulin erased the chances of death from diabetes. This is far from the truth. At present in Minnesota diabetes is about the seventh most important cause of death; about 2 per cent of all deaths are attributed to this disease. Statistics of this sort fluctuate somewhat with the method of gathering them and with the assumptions involved, but diabetes is still an important disease, particularly among the aged.

The frequency of diabetes may be expected to increase for two reasons. The general improvement of life expectancy allows more people to arrive at the age at which their genetic potentiality for diabetes can be expressed. The second reason derives from the success of insulin: diabetics who previously died before reaching the reproductive age now often survive and bear children, who thus "spread" the genes involved. New mutations continuously transmute normal genes to those for diabetes, which are no longer eliminated by the early death of an affected child as frequently as before the use of insulin. Strictly speaking, insulin is a dysgenic agent.

I do not claim particularly close relationship with hamsters, or other laboratory animals, although I admit similarities. It is reasonable that information obtained about heredity in hamsters may give important insights about our own genetics. Meier and Yerganian (1961) have studied extensively the diabetes that appeared in their Chinese hamsters. Four inbred lines were produced with 65 to 90 per cent incidence and great severity. There seems to be a recessive gene with primary responsibility for the potential disease, and its degree of penetrance is enhanced when the over-all genetic background of the animals reaches 65 per cent, or higher, homozygosity. The over-all genetic constitution of a litter governs the degree to which the metabolic disturbance is expressed. Usually the diabetes manifests itself only in adult life (over four to six weeks of age), except for a mild to moderately severe form in one line that appears as early as 18 days. It is interesting that the number of fetuses carried by diabetic mothers was larger than in normal animals.

What do we know about the nature of the possible genetic basis for human diabetes? Pincus and White (1933 and 1934) hold priority for the attempt to analyze the pedigrees according to the age distribution of the members. Such age corrections are absolutely essential for genetic studies of any noncongenital disease. They concluded that the disease was probably determined by a single recessive gene in the homozygous condition. With the passage of time it has become clear that common diseases should be expected to be dependent upon genes at different loci on the same or different chromosomes. This expectation does *not* invalidate the mendelian laws, but it does introduce a heterogeneity into the comparisons of pedigrees from different families. Nonetheless, Steinberg (1959) made a strong case for the major importance of a single locus in his calculations for the expectations of diabetic children when both parents are diabetic. After the age corrections for the children have been made for the data from the available literature (his Table 3), it can be seen that there were 47 diabetic offspring observed when 43.2 were expected on the basis of homozygosity of a single pair of genes. Unless the homozygous genes were the same in both diabetic parents, we would not expect to get diabetic offspring. The agreement between observation and expectation is excellent. It is possible that some polygenic system is present that mimics ordinary single-gene recessive heredity, but such a system could never be explained for counseling purposes and there is no convincing evidence that such a system is present.

We must not forget the twin data. Berg (1939) and Joslin (1940) have presented samples of unselected twin pairs of which at least one member had diabetes. Table XIII shows the combined data from these authors. The concordance of both types of twins would be greater if they had completed their life spans. As it is, it demonstrates a strong genetic background and also environmental influences, which prevent expression of the gene in the one-third of the genetically identical twins who were still discordant when the studies were made. Furthermore, Berg found in her material that if the identical twins lived to be 43 years old, both developed diabetes in every case.

The difficulties that diabetic women have in producing

TABLE XIII   The Strength of Heredity in Diabetes Mellitus (from Berg [1939] and Joslin [1940])

	Both Twins with Diabetes	One Twin with Diabetes
Identical	42 (65%)	23
Fraternal	21 (18%)	95

normal children are well known. Even in latent diabetic women pregnancy may be a dangerous stress to the pancreas. According to Jackson (1955), prediabetes plus pregnancy may result in embryopathy. It is clearly the maternal genotype that disturbs fetal development and results in abortion more often than would be expected due to chance. Counseling in this situation is rather difficult because the counselor has little comprehension of the feelings of the diabetic mother. She may well think that her diabetes is enough of a problem without taking on an increased risk of abortions that are also due to her diabetes. If she has a more optimistic personality and only mild diabetes, she could be encouraged to try to have a family as long as her optimism persists. If the mother has severe diabetes, the situation deteriorates; Grunnet (1957) suggested that therapeutic abortion should be encouraged, particularly if a diabetic child has been produced already. Even though insulin works, diabetes is not something that one would elect.

What empiric risk figures can we find for use in genetic counseling?

There are now many large studies on the expected appearance of diabetes in the siblings of a patient. These are in general agreement, and the calculations from the data of Harris (1950) made by the writer for the previous edition of this book are still valid and applicable. The results are presented in Table XIV. It may be seen that if a sib of a patient manages to live to

TABLE XIV   Empiric Risk Figures for Expectation of Diabetes in the Sibs of the Propositi

| | Age of Onset of Sibs | | | | | | | | |
	0–9	10–19	20–29	30–39	40–49	50–59	60–69	70–79	Total
No. of sibs	3,644	3,502	3,163	2,670	1,977	1,180	425	51	
Diabetics	11	13	17	28	32	39	23	3	166
Risk figures	0.003	0.004	0.005	0.010	0.016	0.033	0.054	0.059	0.184

the age of 80, the chance is 18 per cent that he will have developed diabetes. This figure, incidentally, is the same as that found for fraternal twins, although not all of the twins could have lived until they were 80 years old. If the sibling lives to 70, the chance is 12.5 per cent of developing the disease. It is not unreasonable to expect an average life span of 70 years in the near future.

It is of more importance to have empiric risk figures for the onset of diabetes in the children of a diabetic patient, as this is the question most frequently presented. We know that a diabetic mother has an increased risk of an abortion, but what is the probability that her normal child will develop diabetes during its lifetime? One way to do this is to follow up the children of patients who were treated just after insulin had become established as a universally known therapeutic agent. Such patients would have children by now of the same average age as the patients were when treated in the late twenties. One attempted follow-up is a still unpublished study by my student, Kenneth Derifield. His results are as follows: The incidence of diabetes was determined among the 332 known offspring of 80 persons who were diabetic patients at the Minneapolis General Hospital between the years 1920 and 1926. The age of onset of the disease in the 80 patients ranged from 8 to 75 years, with an average of 46 years. Some 88 per cent of their children have reached the age at which their parents developed the disease, as the parents were all hospitalized from 36 to 42 years ago. In the total group of 332 children there have been 34 diabetics, or 10.2 per cent. If only those offspring are considered who have already reached the age at which the parent developed the disease, or have become diabetic before that age, a figure of 13.2 per cent affected is obtained. The diabetic can be told that the chance that each one of his offspring will eventually become diabetic is between 10 and 15 per cent.

Post and White (1958) assumed that about five per cent of the population has the genotype for diabetes (dd), if it is granted that a single pair of recessive genes is the major etiologic factor. It follows that 20 to 25 per cent of the population are carriers of the gene (Dd). Such a high frequency of carriers for a clearly deleterious gene is evidence of genetic polymorphism. This means that under some conditions the diabetic or the carrier has a reproductive advantage over the normal noncarrier that balances the deaths of those diabetics who have not completed their families. Post and White have attempted to find evidence for genetic polymorphism with some success.

Post and White found that if both parents are diabetic, an average of 5.3 children are produced; if one parent is diabetic, the average is 5.0 children; if neither parent is diabetic, there are 4.6 children. These figures cannot be accepted at their face value, as no childless matings were included and these should affect these averages very significantly. However, the values are in the right direction, and the differences do not need to be this great to contribute to a polymorphic equilibrium. It is also known that diabetic children have an early adolescent growth spurt and presumably earlier sexual maturity. Post and White found that the menarchial age of 219 girls who developed diabetes at age 18 or over was 12.84 years. This menarchial age was younger than that of five groups of college girls that were available as controls. Larger and more elaborate studies are needed, as diabetes is an important disease that will increase in frequency for many years.

In summary, the problem of counseling for diabetes is complicated by two factors: (1) insulin is successful in saving the life of the diabetic in most of the severe cases and gives practically a normal life expectancy; (2) the gene for the disease is so common that the diabetic has a good chance of marrying a carrier. If a normal person is worried because there is diabetes in some relative, his anxieties can be dispelled by pointing out that every large kinship can be expected to have a diabetic member. The general recommendation for the diabetic person would be for some restraint in family size, as it would be an injustice both to society and to the children to produce very many diabetic offspring. The appropriate degree of restraint will depend upon the individual situation, as always. The reader can find an elegant discussion of the eugenic aspects of diabetes by Neel in the American Journal of Human Genetics for December, 1962.

ILLUSTRATIVE EXAMPLES

1.   *Request.*
         A 24 year old Roman Catholic mother came to the Dight Institute after several years of trouble because two of her four children had fibrosis of the pancreas. One of the sick children had died, but the other child was still living at the age of six, though half of its life had been spent in hospitals. The expenses each year had been much greater than the family's total income, and they lost their automobile, their small house and finally their ambition.

         The more recent expenses were borne by "county papers." The county had a legal claim to any property or savings they might be able to accumulate. When the child died and his expenses ceased, they could escape their debt by moving out of the state—a solution they considered dishonest and unacceptable. Since the mother had already had two fibrotic children, she was no longer in the market for the "lightning never strikes twice in the same place" myth. She had already made her decision that her two normal children and the two defective ones were all that she was having. After coming to this conclusion, she asked her priest for a solution to her problem. The priest agreed that the rhythm method would not be practical for a woman with her irregular menstrual cycle and high fertility. The only other solution that the priest could offer was that the couple no longer live together as man and wife. She pointed out to the priest that they enjoy a good family life and that, in view of the remaining 20 years of fertility she might expect to have, his answer was of no help.

         The woman came to the Dight Institute as a final check on what she had learned about the heredity of the disease before going ahead with a sterilization procedure. She explained that contraceptives were not acceptable to her, as their use would involve continuous sinning, while sterilization involved sinning only once. She considered it an even greater sin to risk having further defective children who would suffer and die, while also depriving their normal brothers and sisters of their rightful socioeconomic positions in the community.

Reply.

Her one in four chance of another sick child at each subsequent pregnancy was confirmed. There was little else for us to say. This woman had reached her crossroads before she came to us. She had made her choice between her two sins, the continuing one of subsequent pregnancies, with the risk of a third defective child, or that of sterilization. Anyone can appreciate her dilemma, but no one can decide for her which alternative to accept.

2. *Request.*

A minister of a church in a small rural Minnesota community saw an article by the writer about fibrocystic disease in the Sunday paper. He presented the following case:

"Our 22 month old daughter entered the University Hospital on December 14, 1953, after five weeks in the Community Hospital in F., with recurring pneumonia. After two weeks in the University Hospital, Dr. K. in pediatrics diagnosed her case as fibrocystic disease. She is failing rapidly and is back under oxygen in F. Hospital again, as the Terramycin is no longer holding the lung infection.

"We asked specifically regarding the hereditary aspects of the case and understood that we need not be concerned about future children. But your article, doubtless based on more recent findings, reverses this conclusion."

Reply.

A check with Dr. K. reveals that your daughter does have fibrocystic disease. We are greatly embarrassed that he was not familiar with the hereditary aspects of this disease.

As you know from the newspaper article, the chance is one in four of subsequent children having this same disease. Semiadoption could be considered as a solution of your problem, as it would reduce the chances of another child with this disease from one in four to less than one in a hundred.

3. In 1949 a student came in to see about his problem of getting a family. His wife has diabetes and lost her first two pregnancies, as is often the case. They had decided to have no children of their own but to try to adopt some instead, if the counselor thought that such would be feasible.

Request.

What are the possibilities of obtaining a family by adoption?

Reply.

It was recommended that instead of trying to obtain babies for adoption, older children and perhaps some with different racial mixtures be sought.

Follow-up.

In 1954 the student and his wife startled the counselor by appearing with a completed family of four children, ages 3 to 13 years, which they had accumulated and adopted. It was a happy, lively family, and it was hard to tell who was more pleased about the situation, the children, the parents, or the counselor. The counselor was surprised that his suggestion had been carried out so extensively and successfully.

Chapter 13

MORE "CURES" FOR GENETIC DISEASES

(Pyloric Stenosis and Congenital Dislocation of the Hip)

In Chapter 12 three diseases were considered that seem to have a simple recessive heredity, although it should be remembered that individual families might be expected to show some other genetic mechanism and that in a few cases the disease might result from some purely environmental accident. However, a genetic interpretation for their etiology is more reasonable than any other. The palliatives for P.K.U., fibrocystic disease and diabetes represent amazing medical triumphs; they are not, however, completely effective, and they will contribute to an increase, in the population, in the frequencies of the relevant genes. The traits to be considered in this chapter also seem to have relatively simple genetic backgrounds, although fewer studies have been carried out to demonstrate the genetic mechanisms involved. The medical management of the traits to be considered now is more efficient than it is for those reviewed in Chapter 12, but it likewise contributes to an increase in the frequency of the relevant genes, as will be shown very objectively by the affected offspring of the patients who were operated on for hypertrophic pyloric stenosis.

Hypertrophic Pyloric Stenosis

This disease is often called *congenital* hypertrophic pyloric stenosis. However, there is no really valid distinction between the congenital and the later-developing disease, if we properly deemphasize the significance of the act of birth. Many people have the mistaken concept that diseases present before birth are hereditary, whereas those appearing post partum are not. Actually the fleeting moment of birth is of small consequence in the long period of development of diseases with hereditary backgrounds. There are many diseases, such as Huntington's chorea, which are inherited in a strictly dominant fashion and the genes for which are present at conception, yet there may be no detectable expression of the gene until the person has reached old age.

Congenital pyloric stenosis has been diagnosed as early as seven days after birth, and it has been found in premature babies before the date at which birth would normally have occurred. It has been shown that the condition may develop later in children who showed no radiologic evidence of the disease in the latter part of the first week of life. No different varieties have been noted; the tumors seem to differ only in size and vascularity. A number of studies that have been done establish the incidence of hypertrophic pyloric stenosis at between 2.8 and 4.0 per 1,000 live births. There is general agreement that close to 80 per cent of all affected children are males. Clinical manifestations of the disorder do not develop after the end of the fourth month.

The foregoing observations have significant implications for the geneticist. The excess of affected males does *not* indicate recessive sex-linked heredity, as the number of affected sons born to affected fathers rules out X-chromosome transmission. It does agree with the situation in regard to many human traits in that it is sex-influenced; that is, one sex or the other is more likely to display the trait, and the difference with other traits is often similar to the 4:1 deviation shown with pyloric stenosis.

As many females as males have the genetic basis for the disease, but the differences of physiology or anatomy of females protect them from the expression of the gene more often than is the case in males. The anatomic differences of the female pelvis are an obvious reason for the more frequent expression of congenital dislocation of the hip in girls than in boys. We don't know why boys are more likely to have pyloric stenosis than girls, but it is only reasonable to assume that this trait is sex influenced.

Pyloric stenosis, when expressed, was formerly often lethal, but now many children survive the Ramstedt operation. If there is an important gene involved, and if it has always been expressed and lethal, one would expect it to have a frequency determined by its mutation rate. The high frequency of 4.8 affected per 1,000 live births for boys is higher by far than the probable mutation rate, which indicates that any assumed gene for the disease is protected by environmental factors in many cases. It is even possible that persons with the genotype for the disease who do not die from it are reproductively superior to those without the pyloric stenosis genotype, and thus a genetic equilibrium is produced. We would not expect increased consanguinity in the parents of patients with such a high frequency of the trait, and no increase in the proportion of consanguineous marriages was found in a careful search by McKeown, Mac-Mahon and Record (1952). They also showed that environmental factors do have an important role in the expression of the disease, in that the incidence per 1,000 live births, with the sexes combined, drops from 4.3 for the first-born child to 1.4 for the fourth and subsequent births.

The data derived from twins are not very satisfactory for pyloric stenosis. The high concordance observed for identical twins in the old literature is partly the result of statistical bias in the selection of the twins. MacMahon and McKeown (1955) successfully eliminated this bias by means of their complete sample of pyloric stenosis cases in the Birmingham area from which they selected all the twins with at least one member affected. They had no knowledge as to which twins were identical and which fraternal, other than that based on the sex of the individuals constituting the pairs. Table XV presents the calculated data for their 65 pairs of twins, of which 18 pairs were assumed to be identical and all four of the concordant like-sexed twins were considered to be so. Even on this basis, the evidence for genetic factors is not strong, although it is present. The number of concordant pairs (6) is too small to tell us very much about anything, other than that concordance of the identical twins is small. This must be the case, however, with a trait such as pyloric stenosis, in the etiology of which birth order and sex influence are clearly demonstrated factors. More useful information for counseling comes from the Birmingham studies of the siblings of affected children. There were 12 (9.8 per cent) affected among the 122 brothers born subsequent to the index case, and 2 (1.7 per cent) affected out of 119 subsequent sisters of the propositis. Thus, the empiric risk of being affected is about 1 in 10 for boys, and 1 in 50 for girls.

The kind of experiment that is music to the geneticist's ears is that carried out by Carter (1961). It was possible to trace 562 surviving males and 96 surviving females who had undergone the Ramstedt operation between 1920 and 1940 at The Hospital for Sick Children, London. So far, 174 of the male patients and 48 of the female patients have had at least one child. The

TABLE XV   An Unbiased Selection of Twins, at Least One with Pyloric Stenosis (Adapted from MacMahon and McKeown)

	Both Twins with Pyloric Stenosis	One Twin with Pyloric Stenosis
Identical	4 (22%)	14
Fraternal	2 (4%)	45

results are striking: the female patients produced three or four times more affected children than did the male patients. This might seem incomprehensible, but it is not surprising for a trait in which the threshold to be exceeded to get an affected female is much greater than that for an affected male. An affected female will have more modifying factors for the disease and will transmit more of these to her offspring than will an affected male. The female patients had 44 sons, of whom 9 (20.5 per cent) were affected, and 36 daughters, of whom 4 (11.1 per cent) were affected. The male patients had 162 sons, of whom 11 (6.8 per cent) were affected, and 161 daughters, of whom only 2 (1.2 per cent) were affected.

A final note concerning the histology of hypertrophic pyloric stenosis is probably of some significance for the genetics of the disease. Rintoul and Kirkman (1961) studied the myenteric plexus by biopsy and found that the (Dogiel) Type I neurons were virtually absent from the pylorus of the patients. It is uncertain whether the absence of the Type I cells results from degeneration of these cells or from their failure to develop. My speculation is that a dominant gene prevents the development of these cells whenever the appropriate modifying genes are present and the environmental factors are conducive to the inhibition of the development of the Type I cells.

In summary, this is a most interesting trait about which we have much more to learn. For the moment, we can restate the conclusion of the first edition of this book, which was that we have here heredity of the dominant type with a physiologic limitation of the trait to the male sex in 80 per cent of the cases. The dominant gene has only about 20 to 25 per cent penetrance; its expression is inhibited by other genes and by environmental factors. The chance that the disease will be repeated in subsequent male siblings of a patient is about 1 in 10 and in female siblings about 1 in 50. If the patient reproduces, we can expect 15 per cent affected children from a female patient and 5 per cent affected offspring from a male patient. There is a higher frequency of the disease in first-born children, so one could suggest, with partial tongue in cheek, that women patients have no first-born offspring.

Congenital Dislocation of the Hip

This defect was described by Hippocrates and is one of the common malformations. Its hereditary background was recognized as early as 1678 by Ambroise Paré. No study using modern genetic techniques appeared until 1958, when Record and Edwards presented their findings for Birmingham. They found an incidence of 0.2 and 1.1 per 1,000 for males and females, respectively. Among some other groups the incidence is considerably higher as will be mentioned later. The dislocation usually occurs during the first two years, although it may occur many years later.

Idelberger (1951) collected the data from various sources and found 7,126 boys to 38,485 girls affected, a ratio of 1:5.4. Of a sample of 16,343 cases, 6,558 (40.1 per cent) had both hips affected, 4,376 (26.8 per cent) had the right hip affected and 5,409 (33.1 per cent) had the left hip affected. These variations in expression of the abnormality are frequent characteristics of the common hereditary malformations. Apparently they are attributes of the physiology of normal development. It is thought that the greater frequency of luxation in girls is due to a slight difference in the shape of the pelvis in the two sexes.

There is not complete agreement in the literature as to how the malformation comes about, but an attractive description is that of Hart (1947). He stated that the hereditary factor is not concerned with the dislocation but rather with a primary hip and acetabular dysplasia. Defective ossification results in a flat acetabulum, which is the primary condition. Whether one or both hips become dislocated depends upon environmental factors.

We return to Idelberger (1951) for a large twin series, which clearly shows the presence of an hereditary factor. Because of the rather low concordance (42 per cent) of the identical twins, the importance of environmental factors in the etiology of the disease is obvious. The twin data follow:

	Both Twins Affected	One Twin Affected
Identical	12 (42%)	17
Fraternal	3 (2.7%)	106

If one considers only the cases in which the hip is actually dislocated, a sporadic picture is observed and the inclination is to accept an hypothesis of recessive heredity, as has been done by several authors. It would be more fruitful, though, to consider the heredity of the primary dysplasia of the acetabulum. Obviously such a genetic study cannot be done without radiologic surveys of whole families. Such a study was made by Faber (1937) on a small scale with 10 pedigree groups. Inspection of his pedigrees, which show the persons affected with dysplasia as well as those with actual dislocations, suggests that the dysplasia is inherited as a good clear-cut dominant. The only doubt in the present writer's mind comes from the excess of affected individuals found in the progeny of affected persons. A tabulation of the offspring of affected persons showed 112 with dysplasia or actual dislocation to 88 persons without either. We must subtract the 10 affected who were propositi, which leaves 102 affected to 88 normal, still an excess of affected. The excess might be due to statistical fluctuations, bias in selection of the 10 families to be tested or subjective errors in classifying the x-ray pictures.

If Faber's x-ray classification has any validity at all, it is clear that the acetabular dysplasia does depend upon a single dominant gene with perhaps occasional lack of penetrance. Whether or not the dysplasia is followed by an environmental accident causing a dislocation is of less interest to the geneticist.

He should point out, nonetheless, the possible prophylactic value of knowing that half the children of a person with dysplasia will likewise have the dysplasia.

It might be noted that while the usual sex ratio of dislocated hip cases is almost 6 females to 1 male, Faber's data give a ratio of 1.7 females to 1.0 males when the classification is made according to the x-ray pictures that pick up the dysplasias. This difference in percentages indicates the importance of the normal difference in shape of the female pelvis from that of the male in permitting a higher frequency of dislocations.

Perhaps a suggestion regarding the prophylactic diagnosis of the dysplasia would not be out of order. The anatomic defect of the acetabulum is probably present at birth and could be detected radiographically then or as soon after birth as convenient. If a defect is discovered, the parents could be warned that immediate medical inspection would be mandatory following all accidents and even apparently insignificant falls. It is not suggested that all babies be subjected to radiographic scrutiny— only those where there has been a case of congenital dislocated hip in the family of either parent within, say, the first degree of relationship.

How will the physician know that there has been a case of dislocated hip within the family group? The only way that he can find out is to have the expectant mother dig up the data for her family and that of her husband. It should be ascertained whether there has been a case of clubfoot, harelip, central nervous system abnormality or dislocated hip among the children of the close relatives. It should be pointed out to the expectant mother that congenital malformations are frequent in the population, but by no means inevitable. They are not a disgrace and the parents are not "to blame" for them, even though both parents may make a genetic contribution to the unfortunate victim of the particular defect. This type of family history would be of great value in bringing to the attention of the physician the anxieties that the mother is probably concealing respecting the chances that her baby will show the same defect as some relative. Usually her fears will be greater than necessary. The physician can at one and the same time dispel some of the anxiety and also prepare her for misfortune should it come, as sometimes it must.

It is clear that environmental influences are very important in determining whether the genotype for dislocation of the hip will be expressed. Fortunately, there are special opportunities for making significant studies of such influences. McDermott, Deuschle, Adair, Fulmer and Loughlin (1960) have published a preliminary note on an extensive program concerned with the trait among Navajo Indians, where the prevalence rate is about 1 per cent. Expression of the trait depends in large part upon use of the cradleboard. Affected males are greatly handicapped in their essential horseback riding. Yet there seems to be no social pressure against the disease, it being considered a "relative blessing," in that when evil visited the family this was the worst it could do. Further reports on these Indian pedigrees should be most instructive, at least until the Indians abandon the cradleboard. The typical Navajo family is composed of the father, mother, several children, a Harvard anthropologist and, finally, a physician from the Cornell Medical Center.

Record and Edwards (1958) presented evidence that breech deliveries are an important factor in the expression of the trait in England and that babies born from October through March are more susceptible than those born during the less chilly months. They also point out that associated defects are more frequent than expected among the patients and also possibly among the siblings of the patients. It is difficult to understand the significance of these findings by themselves, but they provide hints as to experimental work that might show the relationship between the environmental factors involved and the development of the trait.

The only unbiased data available for genetic counseling are those given by Record and Edwards (1958). They had no radiologic information concerning the relatives, so the picture they present understates the importance of the problem. Their values are low also because the siblings have not all reached the age of onset, which may not be until adult life in some cases. Presumably clients do not want the most favorable odds; instead, they want to know the worst possible risks so that if they do decide to take a chance, they have a small margin of safety.

The results from the publication of Record and Edwards show 1 affected sibling in 28, or 3.6 per cent, where the patients were boys and 10 affected siblings in 194, or 5.2 per cent, where the patients were girls. Thus, the risk of subsequent children in the family being affected is in the vicinity of 5 per cent. If there is an essential dominant gene, only half the siblings would have the gene; therefore, expression in them would be about 10 per cent of the possible expression with complete penetrance. However, no one should expect complete penetrance in a gene that is highly deleterious in the heterozygous condition and much more frequent in the population than its mutation rate would predicate. The protective decrease in penetrance is provided by other modifying genes and environmental influences.

In summary, the chance of having a second child with congenital dislocation of the hip is about 5 per cent at each subsequent pregnancy. Presumably a person with acetabular dysplasia might expect to have 5 per cent of his children affected. If the child is a girl, the chances that she will be affected are about six times as great as those for a boy. If the family history of either member of a married couple gives evidence of a dislocated hip, then the girl babies, at least, should be examined radiographically for possible acetabular dysplasia. Many of the examinations will give negative results. The medicine of the future will be *preventive* medicine, and the physician should experience gratification and pleasure when the results are negative rather than positive.

ILLUSTRATIVE EXAMPLES

1.   *Request.*
          A physician who learned about the Dight Institute through the first edition of this book presented the sort of pedigree expected for dominance with lack of penetrance in pyloric stenosis. He has three nieces and three nephews. Two of his three nephews underwent the Ramstedt operation, which he attended. One of several first cousins once removed also had pyloric stenosis. He has one child, a daughter, who had the usual feeding problems, which resolved themselves, and pyloric stenosis was not proved. They are afraid that their next child will be a boy. The couple needed a little assurance that the probability of an affected child was not quite as great as their family pedigree would indicate.

     Reply.
          It was pointed out that studies published since the first edition of this book have not changed the general expectations significantly. However, as transmission to his children of a primary dominant gene would be through the father, and not through his wife, the expectation of an affected child might be zero and at worst would be not more than 5 per cent. If the worst did occur, he would be prepared to have immediate treatment provided for the child. Thus, his situation is interesting rather than alarming.

2.   *Request.*
          The daughter of a Minnesota physician developed a bad case of congenital dislocation of the hip when two years old. Shortly before his second daughter was born, the physician had read the chapter related to this trait in the first edition of this book. Stimulated by the plea, in the counseling chapter, for precautionary x-ray pictures, he had her x-rayed before she left the hospital; to his surprise, he found she had acetabular dysplasia. Treatment was prompt and successful. At this point he contacted the writer.

     Reply.
          There was little to add to what he had read. However, he pointed out that his sister had developed congenital dislocation of the

hip at age 21, and his later probings had resulted in determination of the condition in an uncle who had always had "arthritis" in one hip. There have been several subsequent contacts with the physician, and it is fortunate that the theory of dominant inheritance of the acetabular dysplasia had been given from the beginning, as his third child, a daughter, was found to be affected, as well as his fourth child, a son. Treatment was successful for both, and his wife wishes to persevere toward her goal of six children. He does not consider reaching this goal to be as urgent as in the past.

Chapter 14

STILL MORE "CURES"
FOR GENETIC DISEASES

*(Rheumatic Fever and
Tuberculosis)*

Rheumatic Fever

As with clinical medicine, a great diversity of opinion, whether in regard to etiology or to treatment of a disease, usually indicates a lack of adequate basic information or else the unknowing inclusion of several entities as one disease. The conflicting opinions regarding genetic factors in rheumatic fever stem from the difficulty in analyzing a disease in which (1) environmental factors are known to play a role, (2) age of onset varies, (3) clinical appearance of affected individuals varies widely and (4) more girls are affected than boys.

The problem has been studied for the last 100 years. The early references cite striking cases of "rheumatic families" and refer to the high incidence of positive family histories of rheumatic fever patients.

Because of the well-known difficulties of ascertaining and expressing the amount of rheumatic fever occurring in a community or of the proportion of people who suffer from heart damage resulting from rheumatic fever, it is difficult to get estimates of the incidence of the disease in any area at present. It is said to be rare in the tropics and in the arctic. It is certainly common in temperate areas and in the United States. Uchida (1953) estimated a frequency of 4.6 per 1,000 persons in Toronto. A state-wide survey of Minnesota in 1955 uncovered 1.7 cases per 1,000 children under age 16. It is the second highest cause of death in children from 5 to 19 years of age, which makes it an unusually distressing disease. There is a high frequency of the disease among the Puerto Rican immigrants in New York City, although it is thought that the frequency is low in Puerto Rico. This would indicate the importance of environmental factors related to the geographic area.

Post-mortem findings suggest that many more people than those who are known to have had juvenile rheumatism or clinical rheumatic heart disease during life have lesions on or at the base of the heart valves that have the typical histology of rheumatic lesions. Hall and Anderson (1943) have suggested that such lesions may represent infections in the majority of individuals who are resistant, while well-developed endocarditis may be the end result of the same experience in susceptible individuals. It is probable that in susceptible persons the disease is "set off" by a group A beta hemolytic streptococcus infection. The remaining problem, for us, is to determine the nature of the genetic mechanism behind the susceptibility to the streptococcus.

While twin studies ordinarily do not include long follow-ups, they do show a contrast between identical and fraternal pairs indicative of an hereditary background of susceptibility to the bacterium concerned. The rather low concordance of the identical twins seems difficult to explain entirely as a failure of one of the twins to become infected with the agent. Some of the environmental factors involved, therefore, may be very subtle

in their action and difficult to detect. The tabulation of 284 twin
pairs reported by 13 different groups is given below:

	Both Twins with Rheumatic Fever	One Twin Only with Rheumatic Fever
Identical	35 (28%)	92
Fraternal	11 (7%)	146

The disease is sex-influenced to a small, though statistically
highly significant, degree. The ratios reported are from 1.25 girls
to 1.0 boy to 2.5 girls to 1.0 boy. Heredity for susceptibility to
the organism is thus expressed more often in girls than in boys.

The most recent large study of rheumatic fever is that of
Stevenson and Cheeseman (1956), who followed up the siblings
of patients studied in 1950–51. There were 462 families included,
with an index patient in each plus the brothers and sisters, making a total of 2,028 "children" studied. If neither parent was
affected, 6.4 per cent of the siblings of the patient had the disease. Where one parent had the disease, 11.6 per cent of the
siblings were affected. These values are far below the 25 and 50
per cent affected siblings expected for recessive inheritance of a
single gene pair with complete penetrance. Part of the reason for
this is that the values have not been corrected for the proportion
of the patient's sibs who have not yet reached the age of onset
and who will become affected in the future.

The reader should realize by now that with a trait such as
susceptibility to rheumatic fever, which is definitely dependent
upon environmental factors and probably upon an infection, it
will be difficult to determine whether the basic heredity is due to
a dominant gene with low penetrance or due to a recessive gene
with somwhat higher penetrance, or due to a polygenic system
with no single pair of genes being any more important than any
other pair.

A second part of the paper by Stevenson and Cheeseman (1956) is particularly valuable for counseling persons who have had rheumatic fever and are about to start their reproductive life. It is a follow-up of 51 women who had rheumatic heart disease between 1934 and 1941. Of the 51 women, 7 have produced 10 affected children and 28 so far unaffected children, or 26 per cent so far affected. However, we have to add families of the 44 affected mothers who have not yet had an affected child. When this is done, we find that there were 10 affected children in a total of 156, or only 6.4 per cent affected; that is, the risk of the disease *per child* of an affected mother is roughly 6 per cent. But the likelihood of an affected person having *at least* one affected child would be 7 mothers divided by 51 mothers, or a minimum of 13.7 per cent. This figure is a minimum because it has not been corrected for age of onset.

Gould and Read (1940) showed that about half of the cases of rheumatic fever appear after age 15. An appreciable proportion of the cases began when the patient was between 25 and 45 years of age. Thus, one has either to make an age-of-onset correction or to wait and follow up the families many years after the original study.

Studies by Gray, Quinn and Quinn (1952) and by Wilson and Sweitzer (1954) should be mentioned. Their data fit the expectations for simple recessive heredity. The data from these two sources are better than those of Stevenson and Cheeseman, in that their populations are older, but they are worse, in that they clearly have a selection of "loaded" families. The Wilson and Sweitzer sample is unrepresentative, as 8 of their 291 families showed both parents of the patient to be affected. In the 8 families there were 15 children, of whom 14 already had rheumatic fever.

In summary, the precise genetic mechanism responsible for susceptibility to rheumatic fever is not known, although the high frequency of affected children when both parents had had the disease indicates that the most probable mechanism is a homozygous recessive gene with other less important modifying genes. Presumably there must be an infection, although it is not known how massive this must be. For counseling purposes, we could conclude that there would be about a 10 per cent chance of an affected sibling if neither parent has had the disease and about a 15 per cent chance of an affected sibling if one parent was affected. A patient can expect a 15 to 20 per cent chance of having at least one affected child. Two patients who marry can expect a greater than 50 per cent chance of having each child affected, which indicates the marriage of two affected persons is somewhat undesirable, as rheumatic fever is still a serious disease.

Tuberculosis

Modern genetics is aware of the environment. There is nothing more irritating to a geneticist than to be asked to discuss the question of heredity versus environment, on the assumption that they are mutually incompatible. Both must and do interact and are inseparably intermingled. One can vary the heredity and the environment of a group of organisms and measure the resulting change in the group.

There has been a remarkable change in the environment as it affects the frequency of tuberculosis in this country. Thanks to medical science, the infective organism has fallen upon hard times. Even so, this particular bacillus is in no danger of joining the dinosaurs in extinction. The genetic situation could not be expected to have changed appreciably during the last generation, which saw such extraordinary advances in therapy and prevention of the disease.

Davenport (1923) recognized that the ectomorphic body type was more susceptible to tuberculosis than other body types, although the correlation was far from absolute. The thin body is in general a more favorable environment for the culture of the bacillus. The thin body is genetically determined to a considerable extent, and thus the genes affecting body build are also genes for or against tuberculosis. The genetics of infectious diseases is thus an indirect genetics. But in man most genetics is of the indirect sort. In a complicated organism one cannot expect many characters to be determined by a single-step relationship between gene and character. Such relationships can be found in blood group heredity and elsewhere, but they should not be expected to be universally present.

Lurie et al. (1952) have shown in rabbits that resistance to naturally or artificially acquired tuberculosis is largely controlled by their genetic constitution, although resistance may be overwhelmed by large doses of tubercle bacilli.

Many studies have been made of twins, the most recent large one being that of Kallmann and Reisner (1943). Their material consisted of the complete population of twins in New York, one or both of whom had received treatment for tuberculosis from a public institution.

It will be no surprise to the reader that both one-egg twins become tubercular more frequently than do both two-egg twins as shown below:

	Both Twins with T.B.	*One Twin with T.B.*
Identical	52 (66.7%)	26
Fraternal	53 (23.0%)	177

For two-thirds of the pairs, if one of the identical twins had tuberculosis, the other got it also; but in only about one-quarter (23 per cent) of the fraternal twin pairs did both members

contract tuberculosis. It is true that the environment of identical
twins is somewhat less variable than that of fraternal twins so that
the matter of exposure must be considered. Both identical and
fraternal twins become separated at marriage and thus are about
equally exposed to infection. In the cases in which one identical
twin did *not* expose the other, the second one had tuberculosis
in 61.5 per cent of the cases, nonetheless. When the second fraternal twin was not exposed by the first, only 12.7 per cent developed tuberculosis. The siblings of dizygotic twins are genetically
the same, on the average, as these twins and should have similar
variability in their environments. Consequently, the siblings
should have the same frequency of tuberculosis as that in the
second fraternal twin, and they do. The corrected total morbidity
expectations, as percentages, for the different degrees of relationship to the twins studied by Kallmann and Reisner are shown in
Table XVI.

TABLE XVI   Corrected Tuberculosis Morbidity Rates of Relatives
of Twin Index Cases (Kallmann
and Reisner)

	Incidence per 100
General population	1.4
Husbands and wives	7.1
Half siblings	11.9
Parents	16.9
Full siblings	25.5
Fraternal cotwins	25.6
Identical cotwins	87.3

These figures seem to give a rather gloomy prognosis for
those who have a close relative with tuberculosis. However, they
are not out of line with other studies such as that of Pearl
(1936), who followed up the offspring of tuberculous persons
and found that if both parents had the disease, 35.7 per cent of
their offspring also got it, while if one parent had it, only 13.5
per cent of the offspring developed the disease.

Before giving way to despair over these rather ominous data, one should remember that they are for the last couple of generations when the "white plague" was a national menace. Today, these figures should be considerably reduced, thanks to Christmas seals and the determined campaigns to cut down infection in the general population. Tuberculosis is still a serious killer, but it no longer ranks among the first 10 causes of death in Minnesota.

Anderson, Benjamin, Grenville-Mathers and Trenchard (1957) studied households in England in which there was a patient affected with tuberculosis and examined the other residents of the house, a good proportion of whom were not blood relatives such as husbands or wives. They found that 4.9 per cent of the nonrelatives had or developed tuberculosis, while of the first-degree relatives only 4.5 per cent had or developed it. If this difference has any significance, we are left with the nonsense answer that it is safer to be a blood relative of the patient than a roomer or a spouse. In other words, the roomer and the spouse had more contact with the patient than his parents or his children and were therefore infected more frequently. This could well have been the case, and it illustrates the necessity for rather sophisticated studies to obtain precise answers to the problems of the genetic susceptibility to infections. In this situation the influence of heredity may have been obliterated by the high degree of infectivity to which the contacts had been exposed.

In summary, it is obvious that without infection there can be no tuberculosis. However, at constant dosage of infectivity, unless it is overwhelming, and perhaps sometimes even then, we can expect genetic difference in susceptibility to any infective agent, including the tuberculosis bacillus.

It is unlikely that the susceptibility or resistance to tuberculosis depends upon a single pair of genes. Therefore, if more than one pair of genes is concerned, it falls into the multiple factor type of inheritance. This situation makes life difficult for the geneticist, but it does not decrease the role of heredity by one whit.

A very practical result of the hereditary basis for suscepti-bility to tuberculosis may be seen in the practice of insurance companies in "rating up" children and young adults where there is a history of tuberculosis, because their experience shows a higher mortality up to the age of 35 in the relatives of tubercular persons. Counseling is important as a general warning to the young in such families to take life easy and get their chest films once a year. This should be done according to a schedule and not as a result of fits of worry or depression.

ILLUSTRATIVE EXAMPLE

Once again the counselor can counsel himself. My mother died of tuberculosis when I was six years of age. I was always a spindling child and was about 20 per cent underweight. Long before the word "genetics" was known to me, the fear of developing tuberculosis was present. The situation was not improved by the necessity for "rated-up" life insurance premiums because of this family history.

Eventually, serious concern about tuberculosis was removed by the series of annual clear chest films and the understanding that if genetic susceptibility were present, it might be overruled by proper living. No man can escape his genes, but he can control some of them in some cases.

Chapter 15

HARELIP AND CLEFT PALATE

(of Mice and Men)

Harelip is an important abnormality partly because it is so frequent. This is particularly interesting abnormality because, though complicated, harelip and cleft palate behaves remarkably similarly in both mice and men.

Wisconsin law requires the reporting of all congenital anomalies on the birth certificate by the attending physician. According to Phair (1947), there were 567,509 children born in that state between January 1, 1935, and December 31, 1944, and of these, 736 had harelip and/or cleft palate. This is 0.13 per cent, or 1 in every 770 births. This is the largest and probably the most accurate sampling reported so far, although even this rate is probably too low because of failure to report some mild cases. Kobayasi (1958) reported a frequency of 1 in 500 live births in Japan affected with harelip and/or cleft palate.

The present writer started graduate work as a mouse-lover and presented a study on a new mutation, harelip and cleft palate in the house mouse, for his degree. Consequently, a comparison can be made between his results (Reed, 1936) and those reported by Miss Phair from Wisconsin.

It is not surprising to the geneticist that the defect should express itself about the same in such different types of mammals. We know many such cases of "parallel mutations" to be found in very distantly related organisms. Table XVII gives three variables in the expression of harelip and cleft palate that have been studied in both mice and men. It is clear that in both species there is a similar excess of affected males and of clefts of the left side in unilateral cases. We also find a peculiar relationship between the age of the mother and the frequency of expression of harelip in the offspring. The youngest mothers show a high frequency of harelip, but for unexplained reasons mothers just a little older (3 months in mice, 20 to 24 years in women) show a decided drop in harelip production; this is followed by a sharp rise in the older age groups. Thus, at the age of the mother when the conditions for the production of offspring are optimum, the frequency of harelip is lowest.

The interesting papers of Warkany, Nelson and Schraffenberger (1943) and of Warkany (1953) describing the induction of cleft palate in embryos of rats placed on deficient diets should be considered. The many cases of cleft palate resulting from deficient diets of the mother were morphologically somewhat different from cases in mice dependent upon a genetic background.

TABLE XVII   The Three Variables in the Expression of Harelip and Cleft Palate for Which There Are Adequate Data for Both Mice and Men

	Mice	Men
1. *Sex*		
Excess of affected males	8.3%	10.2%
Deficiency of affected females	8.3%	10.2%
2. *Age of mother* at which a sag in production of harelip occurs, followed by an increase in frequency	3 months	20–24 years
3. *Asymmetry, or excess* of unilateral clefts of the left side compared with the right	5.5%	10.8%

The diet-produced abnormal rats are nonhereditary copies of the hereditary type of abnormality and are referred to by Warkany and geneticists as "phenocopies." There is no inheritance of the phenocopy, but future generations would be expected to produce cleft palate individuals if the dietary deficiency continued. They suggest that clinical material may well be a conglomeration of hereditary cases and phenocopies.

Fraser, Kalter, Walker and Fainstat (1953) and Ingalls, Avis, Curley and Temin (1953) have shown that cortisone and hypoxia, respectively, can cause cleft palate in the mouse embryo and that the frequency with which the defect appears is related to the genetics of the different strains of mice employed.

What is the mechanism for the hereditary cases in man? An answer must be somewhat equivocal for any trait such as this, which clearly shows influences of the environment. Test and Falls (1947) presented a good pedigree of what seems to be clear-cut dominant inheritance. However, this pedigree is probably unique in the collection of pedigrees at the Michigan Heredity Clinic where they work, and we have none like it in our collection at the Dight Institute. For the bulk of the cases, it is clear that the inheritance depends upon some recessive mechanism or upon a dominant with very low penetrance, that is, a dominant gene which seldom causes any deviation from normal development of the mouth. When we qualify to this extent, it means that we don't really know how many genes are involved to a greater or less degree.

It is probable that there is an etiologic difference between clefts of the lip with or without cleft palate and isolated cleft palate. It is also possible that cleft lip and cleft palate associated with several other malformations in the same child represent a third type. The writer will hazard the guess that the monstrosities with cleft lip and many other anomalies (third type) are the victims of gross chromosomal abnormalities. We will know whether this guess is right or wrong within a very few years.

Metrakos, Metrakos and Baxter (1958) sifted the twin literature for unselected cases and added 10 pairs of their own. Their results for cleft lip with or without cleft palate, the first etiologic category, follow:

	Both Twins with Cleft Lip	One Twin with Cleft Lip
Identical	8 (42%)	11
Fraternal	4 (5%)	63

The difference in concordance is significant from two points of view. There is an hereditary background of importance. Yet both identical twins agree in showing the trait less than half the time. Twins are thus very useful in providing a gross evaluation of the relative effects of heredity and environment in determining the variation in expression of the characteristic.

There was once an old Norwegian law which forbade butchers to hang hares in public view for fear that the sight would cause pregnant women to have children with harelip. Environmental influences are important, but it is not likely that they work via the optic nerve!

In my work with harelip in the mouse (1936), it was found that about 83 per cent of the variation in cleft lip frequency was due to environmental factors when the genetic basis had been made fairly homozygous by inbreeding. Of these environmental factors, about 88 per cent were "intangible," which means that they were trivial fluctuations in the uterine environment. Trasler (1960) has shown in the mouse that some of these intangible factors may be associated with the distal (ovarian) uterine position since embryos that implant there have a higher incidence of cleft lip.

There is a very strong correlation in human beings between the type of anomaly in the propositi and that in their relatives. This is shown below and is from the paper by Kobayasi (1958). Thus, the environmental influences affect the degree of expression but not the etiologic type of anomaly.

		Propositi	
		Cleft Lip with or without Cleft Palate	Isolated Cleft Palate
Relatives	Cleft lip with or without cleft palate	83	3
	Isolated cleft palate	2	27

We face, at last, the problem of what to tell the unhappy people who come for counseling. They are unhappy, or they would not have taken the trouble to find the counselor. If the family should present a pedigree of dominance of the trait, like that published by Test and Falls (1947), the counseling will be unequivocal. But it is not likely that such a case will be presented. The usual situation is that of bewildered clients who know of no previous case of cleft lip in their family histories. The problem is *not* whether there is a single recessive gene more important than other recessive modifying genes, compared with a polygenic system where the effect of each pair of genes is small and roughly equivalent to that of each of the other pairs. The two situations will give about the same results according the the calculations of Edwards (1960). The great difficulty is the usual lack of appropriate data in the literature. Furthermore, we cannot tell whether or not the affected child is a phenocopy. But it should be remembered that the environmental factors responsible for a phenocopy may be repeated at the next pregnancy, so the risk for a couple who have had an affected child will seldom be zero for the next child. There is, therefore, no alternative but to use the best empiric risk figures available. It should be remembered that even with a regular dominant gene, where the risk is 50 per cent, the next child will not himself be 50 per cent affected but will have the gene in none of his cells or in 100 per cent of them.

One might think that all one would need to do is to go to the literature, collect the pedigrees given for this trait, and find the percentage of abnormal children born in these families after the first affected child. This must not be done since the answers obtained will usually be incorrect. The literature of human genetics is so hopelessly biased for many traits that it will not give a reasonable answer to our question. The situation is in no way the fault of an individual or a group but a result of the tendency of most workers to publish only those pedigrees that are exceptional because of the large number of affected individuals, in the degree to which they are affected, or even in the type of inheritance involved.

The classic paper on cleft lip and palate in man is that of Fogh-Andersen (1943). It includes the mass of cases treated in Denmark since 1934 and supplemental material on 78 cases of isolated cleft palate found in patients at earlier dates. The beauty of this Danish work is that *all* the pedigrees are presented in pictorial form. In only 1 of the 498 pedigrees was there an unbroken line of cleft lip for as many as three generations without a skip. Thus, dominant inheritance is not of importance in the total picture of cleft lip and palate. Even this elegant study is badly biased in that the child with the cleft was the last sibling in the pedigree much too often. This is because the affected child appeared for his surgery before his subsequent siblings were born. A follow-up study is needed and is being carried on over the years by Dr. Clarke Fraser of McGill University.

The best way to calculate the empiric risk from Fogh-Andersen's data is to take all children born subsequent to the propositi and find the percentage that are affected with clefts. The results from this method, and from several other methods, are demonstrated in detail in my paper in *De Genetica Medica* (Reed,

1961). If one parent is affected and has had an affected child, the risk for each subsequent child is about 16 per cent. If neither parent is affected, the risk subsequent to the propositus is about 7 per cent. The values for isolated cleft palate also show 16 per cent for each child subsequent to the propositus when one parent is affected. Only 1 per cent of the children subsequent to the patient had isolated cleft palate when neither parent was affected. This figure is probably too low.

Another important question comes from the person with the cleft lip who wishes to reproduce. No cases are known to me of any children being produced from a union of two persons with cleft lip. All unions are of an affected person with a normal-appearing person. Fogh-Andersen had a few such data from his propositi, who produced 157 children, including 3 (2 per cent) who had clefts of the lip and palate. This low percentage of affected children from an affected parent probably indicates that few of the spouses of the affected persons carried the various recessive genes necessary for the appearance of the trait. Fraser Roberts (1962) has just published a larger series of observations on children who had one affected parent. He found 10 affected children in a total of 303, or 3.3 per cent.

In summary, it can be predicted that future studies will provide interesting new discoveries as to how both environmental and genetic factors interact in the production of a frequent congenital anomaly such as cleft lip and palate. It is not likely that these discoveries will change the counseling risks very much, as so many factors are involved in the appearance of the trait. The most frequent counseling case will still be that of the normal-appearing parents who had had a child with cleft lip and are anxious to learn what their risk is for each future pregnancy. This will probably still be in the area of 7 to 10 per cent.

ILLUSTRATIVE EXAMPLE

Request.

The mother of a boy with bilateral harelip and cleft palate also has a brother with the defect. Her family is completed, but she has always been troubled by the assumption, though not often voiced, of her husband that she was entirely "to blame" for their son's malformation. "Was the heredity only from my side of the family?"

Reply.

It is, of course, possible that despite the fact that the uncle also had harelip and cleft palate, the child's defect was not of an hereditary nature. However, it is more reasonable to assume that it was hereditary and recessive in its expression. This would mean that your husband also carried a concealed gene for harelip and that his family was equally "responsible" for the son's defect. Husbands seem fairly willing to place "blame" for congenital defects upon the mother, so you can assume that your husband is fairly representative of the species.

Chapter 16

CLUBFOOT

Congenital clubfoot is the most common serious deformity of the foot. The frequency has been estimated at about 1 per 1,000 births by Nilsonne (1927). In about 50 per cent of the cases both feet are affected. Of over 25,000 cases in the literature, 66.2 per cent were males and 33.8 per cent females. The finding of a significant excess of one or the other sex is not unusual for the common congenital anomalies. We have no information as to why one sex should express a character, such as clubfoot, more freely than the other sex. Presumably the different physiologic characteristics of male and female embryos account for the difference in expression. These are differences in the internal environment of the embryo and are important for the degree of expression (expressivity) of the genetic background.

Müller (1926) pointed out that it was recognized a century ago that clubfoot resulted from spastic muscular contraction, the bones being drawn away from their proper positions as a consequence. Possibly the contractions result from some more fundamental nervous anomaly. When spina bifida is also present, as is frequently the case, the clubfoot may merely be the sequel of the nerve damage due to the spina bifida.

The evidence of a genetic background for clubfoot is strong, although the influence of the internal environment of the embryo upon the expression of the character should be emphasized.

A paper by Böök (1948) considered the evidence for a genetic background for congenital clubfoot and quite correctly started by reviewing the research on twins. His Table I, on the expression of clubfoot in the two kinds of twins, is reproduced here as Table XVIII. The identical twins show both members with clubfoot 10 times as frequently as the fraternal twins. Furthermore, Böök showed that the frequency of clubfoot among the sibs of single-birth children affected with clubfoot is 3 per cent, exactly the same figure as that for a second affected twin of the two-egg type. This means that having two embryos in the same uterus does not in itself increase the frequency of expression of clubfoot. It also shows that the gene or genes for clubfoot, when present, are expressed in only about one-third of the embryos (32 per cent) having these genes. Consequently, the internal environment of the embryo is very important in determining whether or not the genes for clubfoot will be expressed.

A study of the frequency of children with clubfoot among the progeny of first cousin marriages was enlightening. Böök found that 27 per cent of the sibs of the clubfoot propositi also had clubfoot in the families where the parents were first cousins. When the parents were not blood relatives, the usual 3 per cent of clubfoot among the sibs of the propositi was observed. This provides a clue to some of the variation in expression of the character. When blood relatives produce children, one expects that some of the recessive genes that were "hidden" in the com-

TABLE XVIII   The Occurrence of Clubfoot in the Two Kinds of Twins

	Both Members with Clubfoot	One Member with Clubfoot
Identical	13 (32%)	27
Fraternal	4 (3%)	130

mon ancestor of the related parents will become expressed in the
visible homozygous form in their children. If a number of sub-
sidiary modifying genes are necessary to give an expression to
the main pair of genes concerned with clubfoot, then the consanguineous marriages could be expected to give a higher frequency of clubfoot offspring; this was observed to be the case.
This represents an additional use for consanguinity studies.

It is possible to add still another tool for the detection of
the influence of heredity in the production of traits with variable
expression. Numerous traits in man are known to have different
frequencies in differerent ethnic groups. In Hawaii the ethnic
origins of each baby are recorded, and it is obligatory to record
also all congenital abnormalities. A study by Stewart (1951)
showed that there were remarkable differences in the frequencies
of three abnormalities among the different racial groups that
make up Hawaii. The anomalies considered were clubfoot, congenital dislocation of the hip, and harelip and cleft palate.

It is very exciting to a geneticist that the remnants of the
"pure" Hawaiians have an extremely high frequency of clubfoot
and of harelip and cleft palate and a remarkable absence of
congenital dislocation of the hip, compared with the part Hawaiians, Caucasians, Chinese and Japanese. This means that the different ethnic groups find themselves with different frequencies
of the genes for these three defects. In Hawaii these sharp differences may well have arisen because of random sampling
among the rather small groups of people who became the ancestors of the present population of the islands.

The data indicated that the genetic background for clubfoot is probably what might be called subrecessive. A single pair
of genes is not sufficient to produce the abnormality alone; one
or more other pairs of genes are necessary to get the maximum
expression of the character. This is obviously an unsatisfactory
way in which to leave the genetics of a character, but because

of the difficulties of studying the genetics of man we must do so for the present.

Clubfoot refers to a host of abnormalities of the foot. No one would expect all the cases to have the same etiology or the same genetics. It is perhaps the most heterogeneous of the traits considered in this book. A recent report by Johnston and McKusick (1962) concerns an interesting pedigree of a sex-linked form of spastic paraplegia. This is the classic type of sex linkage, and the trait was traced back for seven generations to a couple born about 1780. One of the symptoms of the paraplegia is clubfoot, and it is congenital. The clubfoot is merely one manifestation of the neurologic disorder, but it fits the usual broad definition of talipes.

Even though the genetic background for clubfoot has not been subjected to final study, we should be able to calculate the risk figures needed for counseling in medical genetics. The only consideration in the literature of this subject is that by Böök (1948), who collected the data published by three German physicians (Fetscher, Isigkeit and Assum). As mentioned before, they found that the frequency of clubfoot among all the sibs of propositi was 3 per cent when the parents were unaffected. Böök continued and stated that "if the parents are unaffected and already have one child with congenital clubfoot the mean risk of following children being affected is 3 per cent." This statement is not strictly accurate because the 3 per cent includes the children born before the propositi. We are not interested in these previous sibs, as we wish to know only what frequency of clubfooted children were born *subsequent* to the propositi.

Unfortunately, one cannot obtain this figure from the German references as only selected pedigrees were published, usually those with the most cases involved. Such a procedure, in papers purporting to be on genetics, is not excusable. The error stems from the misconception held by many physicians that a character is "hereditary" in only those families where more than one case appears, and that in the one-case families the character is "environmental." This mistaken idea must be eradicated as soon as possible. Nonetheless, it is possible to set the limits between which the correct answer lies.

The least biased of the three German studies seem to be those of Assum (1936). In his pedigrees there were 63 children born after the propositi, of which 5, or 8 per cent, had clubfoot. Therefore, for counseling purposes, we can expect that in subsequent pregnancies, following the appearance of a child with clubfoot, the risk of a repetition is from 3 to 8 per cent.

ILLUSTRATIVE EXAMPLE

Cases like the following keep life from becoming boring. In the preceding paragraphs it was shown that clubfoot is not only subrecessive but also asymmetric and variable in its expression. The B family shows seven cases of bilateral clubfoot with an accompanying split thumb nail. If the nail is kept cut, it is no bother, but it is odd to have this little peculiarity also produced by the heredity for clubfoot.

Request.
We recently had quite a shock in our family when our third child was born, our second boy to be born with bilateral clubfeet. We have quite a family history of this deformity, but we didn't dream it would happen to both our boys. Our question now is, of course, whether or not it is possible for me to give birth to a perfect male child. Is there any assurance that the rest of our children will be normal, or should we not risk having any more children in view of this deformity?

Reply.
Your family tree is quite striking with respect to the clubfoot deformity, for it is unusual to have so many individuals affected. In your pedigree the trait skipped one generation in one instance and two generations in another. From only one pedigree, such as yours, it is difficult to tell whether there is a dominant gene that doesn't always express itself (incomplete penetrance) or whether by coincidence the marriages have been between heterozygous persons in each case

where the defect has occurred. With common anomalies such as club-foot we are always baffled in trying to distinguish between dominance and the coincidence of several marriages between carriers. The better guess here would seem to be dominance with incomplete penetrance; consequently, the prediction is more gloomy than the usual 3 to 8 per cent risk and rises to perhaps 25 per cent risk of bilateral club-foot for your subsequent pregnancies, if any.

First Follow-up.

The lady reported that "My husband feels that we should have more children, so we probably will, in spite of the odds being so much against our having perfectly formed offspring."

The counselor pointed out that the odds were not against her but rather with her. The chances were about three out of four that each child would turn out to be normal; she need not worry unduly about trying again. It was also suggested that her husband needed a little further education, which could be easily provided in this way. The next summer, just as he is about to leave for his annual vacation of fishing in the 10,000 lakes of Minnesota, she should take to her bed with a feigned illness and not set a foot out of it until his vacation is over. He will have to care for the three children during the two weeks and tend her needs as well. She should sleep during the day and be ill most of the night. This is a most educational experience, beneficial for all males who are overly eager for the women to produce and care for large families.

Second Follow-up.

The counselor received a charming little blue card announcing the birth of a perfectly normal girl. The mother thinks she will try the cure on her husband next summer. She expects to be pregnant by then again and so will have a legitimate reason to turn the household chores over to her husband for two weeks.

Third Follow-up.

The mother's expectation of pregnancy was realized, and a normal boy was produced. Four years have passed since then, and no more children are expected.

Chapter 17

ALLERGIES

To touch this subject is to rush in where angels fear to tread. A remarkably large number of scientists have dashed in, nonetheless. We may as well start with a definition of allergy. By allergy is meant an altered response to specific antigens. The concept of allergy includes anaphylaxis, immunity, allergic diseases and latent allergy. We will not be concerned with anaphylaxis nor immunity here, which leaves the problem that of allergic diseases, from a practical point of view.

The familial occurrence of asthma was recognized as early as 1650. In recent years many studies have attempted to demonstrate the heredity of allergic diseases. In such studies some 50 to 70 per cent of the close relatives of the propositi have some allergic manifestation. The fact that 5 to 10 per cent of the general public is also allergic gives immediate notice that because of this high frequency it will be difficult to differentiate between a dominant and a recessive mechanism of heredity. In fact, there are those who presume that every person has a major or minor allergic disposition. If so, the heredity involved concerns merely the *degree* of reaction to the pollen, feathers or other substance. Polygenic heredity seems likely.

Spaich and Ostertag (1936) made a study of twins and separated the index twin according to whether he had hay fever, migraine, urticaria or asthma. The number of pairs of twins for each of the four diseases is not large enough to show which complaint is the more "strongly" inherited. Each gives the usual picture for an hereditary trait, and if they are summated, we get the figures given below. It should be remembered that in this table the concordance is for precisely the same specific allergy the index twin had.

	Both Twins with the Same Allergy	*Only One Twin with the Allergy*
Identical	20 (59%)	14
Fraternal	5 (20%)	20

The results are changed quite remarkably when the second twin is examined for any allergy, not just the one the index case possesses. The concordance then becomes much higher for both the identical and fraternal twins. In fact, for the first time in this book we find more concordant than discordant *fraternal* twins.

	Both Twins with Any Allergy	*Only One Twin with Any Allergy*
Identical	30 (88%)	4
Fraternal	16 (64%)	9

The excess of concordant fraternal twins might indicate dominant heredity, as half of the fraternal cotwins should show the trait if it is dominant. It is more likely that the excess merely means that both the heredity and the irritating agent are unusually prevalent in sibships where one child has had allergic distress. The last point gives no help in trying to decide between dominant and recessive heredity. From a physician's point of view it is not particularly important whether the heredity is dominant or recessive with such a common ailment. As no infection is at the bottom of the problem, the allergies cannot be eliminated with antibiotics, so the frequency of allergic reactions is likely to remain high. The allergist is likely to have plenty of business for some time to come.

It is probable that this selection of twins is highly biased, as is so often the case with the older literature. The 59 pairs of presumably identical twins reported by Bowen (1953) showed concordance in only 7 pairs (12 per cent) for allergic manifestations. Unfortunately, Bowen had no sample of fraternal twins to compare with the 59 identical pairs. His work also ignores the necessary corrections for age of onset.

The exact chance that the allergic parent will have an allergic child is hard to give, because it depends upon the way the problem is stated. In an excellent study by Schwartz (1953) it was found from 191 asthma patients that only 7 per cent of their children had asthma. However, if these figures were corrected for age of onset, the value would be higher. In addition, if vasomotor rhinitis, eczema, urticaria, migraine, Quincke's edema and hay fever in the children are also counted, more than one-fifth of the children are affected. The last figure would also be higher following a correction for age of onset.

It has been generally recognized by physicians that families showing one kind of allergy often display another allergy, and occasionally one person may show as many as four allergies. It was Schwartz's (1953) conclusion that asthma, vasomotor rhinitis, Besnier's prurigo and hay fever depend upon one gene, which obviously shows some lack of penetrance, regardless of whether it behaves as a dominant or a recessive. He thinks that it is possible, but not very likely, that urticaria and Quincke's edema are related to asthma. It is his opinion that eczema, migraine, and gastrointestinal allergy are *not* related to asthma.

One of the more useful studies for counseling purposes is that of Van Arsdel and Motulsky (1959). Their sample of 5,818 college students included 16.7 per cent with asthma and/or "hay fever." This high frequency of allergy is impressive since most of the students grew up and lived in the State of Washington where air-borne pollen and mold-spore concentrations are rarely high and ragweed is nonexistent. A survey of the parents of all the students showed that if both parents were allergic, 58 per cent of their student offspring were likewise allergic; if one parent was allergic, 38.4 per cent of the students were allergic; if neither parent had suffered from asthma or "hay fever," only 12.5 per cent of their student offspring were afflicted.

If we work from the other end, we note that of the 16.7 per cent of the students who were allergic some 36.5 per cent had one or both parents with allergy. Thus, regardless of whether the heredity involved is polygenic, incompletely recessive or dominant, there is a large risk, somewhere between 25 and 50 per cent, that each child of an allergic person will develop allergies. Even if neither member of the couple is allergic, there is a fair chance of an allergic child.

The study mentioned above gives no data for siblings of affected students, so we have no direct estimate of the frequency of allergies among them. We would certainly expect this value to be higher than the 16.7 per cent observed in the entire student population. A conservative speculation that 25 per cent of the siblings of affected students would be affected does not seem to be out of order.

The situation is still fluid. Genetic counseling is rather academic for a trait such as an allergy because of the extraordinarily high frequency of the gene, or genes, concerned. There is a good chance that one can avoid having the heredity for a rare trait, but it is more difficult to escape having an allergy in the family. To eliminate allergies from the population by eugenic means would be quite impossible. It is not likely that we will learn to love the allergies, but we shall probably have to learn to live with them. Modern medicine should make the life of the allergic person much more comfortable than it has been in the past.

ILLUSTRATIVE EXAMPLE

Request.

I have had asthma since I was three years old. My grandfather and cousins on my mother's side had it, but none on my father's side. Now, what I'd like to know is this. If my wife (I have none at present) has had *no* asthmatics in her ancestry, will our children have asthma? I feel that it would be an injustice to a wife and children to marry with that possible heredity characteristic hanging over our heads.

Reply.

It is possible that your prospective wife may fail to materialize, solving your problem of heredity automatically. However, assuming that some young lady does drag you up to the altar, we must prepare you for the future.

Unfortunately, the inheritance of allergic diseases is not well understood. These diseases vary considerably in severity and are very common. The predisposition to allergic diseases is not only very common, but perhaps as much as 10 per cent of the population has major allergic difficulties. Many authors have concluded that the tendency to allergic disease behaves as a dominant trait, and thus it could come down one side of the family and involve the prospective children. The chance that each of your children would have some allergy or other is probably about one in three. This may seem pretty serious, though it should be remembered that one can learn to live with his allergies.

Fortunately, medical research should come to your aid within the next few years with injections that will be much more successful than those now known.

Chapter 18

BLOOD GENETICS

Death is the price of ignorance in blood group genetics! The technician who matches blood types can do so without genetics, but her ritual is precisely determined by the genes. When Jansky and Moss independently gave opposite numbers to the same blood groups, people died from transfusions of the wrong gene products. This fatal confusion was eliminated by the substitution of the A-B-O letter system. The confusion of terminology that existed then was as nothing compared with what it is now for the Rhesus factors. Fortunately, the confusion is now academic and results in no deaths, we hope.

It is interesting that while predictions about the heredity of the blood groups are practically infallible, the *mature* red blood cells, which obey the mendelian laws so nicely, have no power of reproduction, nor do they have nuclei or genes present. The story is that the immature red blood cells once did have genes present that controlled the production of the specific antigens, which exist in the cell as long as it lives. There are probably not many chemical steps between the gene and the antigen. Here is an opportunity for an enterprising biochemist to make his name and fame along the route from gene to antigen!

A person does not have antibodies in his blood that can agglutinate his own antigens. But he has all the rest of the antibodies of the A-B-O system. The AB person has both antigens and consequently no corresponding antibodies. If he had such antibodies, he would be self-eliminating. As he has no antibodies lurking about, he can receive red blood cells from any other type of A-B-O person and is therefore called a "universal recipient." The group O individual has all the antibodies and will coagulate blood from all A-B-O types except his own. He is called a "universal donor" because his red blood cells have no antigens and therefore cannot be agglutinated by any antibodies. The transfusion of O blood introduces into the host all the antibodies there are in the A-B-O series, which, one would think, should coagulate some of the recipient's remaining precious red cells. Why don't they? The answer is that agglutination is a co-operative effect in a way. If the antibodies are too dilute, no agglutination occurs at all. Consequently, when the antibodies are slowly released into the patient's rapidly moving blood stream the antibodies are instantaneously diluted below the minimum strength for agglutination.

One of the recent major advances in medical genetics has been the realization that when there are three or more alleles of one locus present at high frequencies in a population, there must be an equilibrium present that depends upon the selective elimination of each genotype under different conditions. Many geneticists used to think of the A-B-O blood groups as being neutral. We know better now. Many cases of A-B-O incompatibility have been reported recently. Here the mothers are of blood group O, and the maternal antigens destroy the embryos with A or B blood groups in some cases. One of the early statistical demonstrations that such AO and BO embryos were being eliminated in some percentage of the cases of incompatible matings was provided by Matsunaga (1955). His work was with Japanese statistics. Chung and Morton (1961) have applied the segregation analysis technique to Caucasian family data on A-B-O blood groups. Maternal-fetal incompatibility significantly reduced fertility by about 6 per cent and caused elimination of about 9 per cent of *incompatible* zygotes. Such studies indicate that there is an important loss of the A and B alleles during the fetal and postnatal development. Therefore, in order to maintain the frequency of A and B genes in the population, they must be selected for later on in life. If their selective advantage is related to infections rampant in the past but no longer of importance, we could expect the frequency of A and B to decrease in the future. This is, of course, pure speculation—but good fun!

The M-N system of blood groups is sharply different from the A-B-O system in that no one has antibodies against either the M or N antigen and cannot produce them even upon repeated transfusions. Rabbits will produce distinct antibodies against the M and N antigens after a series of injections, and the rabbit antibodies can agglutinate human blood. To distinguish between the genes for M and N antigens in man we are forced to resort to laboratory animals. Except for its usefulness in clarifying paternity disputes and zygosity in twins, the M-N system is mainly of academic interest.

Such is far from the case with the Rhesus factors. In the flush of excitement over the 1940 discovery of this group, the problem of the erythroblastotic baby has probably been somewhat overemphasized. However, to the couple meeting the situation in their own child, there is no lack of seriousness or importance in it. While to some, almost always males, a wasted pregnancy seems to be a minor inconvenience, this view is not shared by the woman who has suffered the experience. To the women who have had erythroblastotic babies, and there are thousands of them, the new understanding of the Rhesus factors comes from one of the brightest pages of science. These women are indebted to many scientists, among whom the names of Landsteiner, Levine and Wiener must not be forgotten.

Landsteiner and Wiener (1940) immunized rabbits and guinea pigs with the blood of Rhesus monkeys and made the surprising discovery that the resulting antibodies agglutinated not only monkey red cells but also the red cells of about 85 per cent of a sample of white persons. The 85 per cent whose red cells were agglutinated by the rabbit anti-Rhesus serum the authors called Rh positive; the remaining 15 per cent were Rh negative. Once when the writer pointed out to a P.T.A. group that about 15 per cent of women are Rh negative, a man challenged the statement by saying, "Doctor, you are wrong. All women are negative!" After the laughed subsided, it was possible to point out that 15 per cent of men are also Rh negative, by way of evening the score.

It is true that the 15 per cent of women who are Rh negative bear the risk of misfortune due to erythroblastosis. Roughly speaking, about 1 in 200 pregnancies results in an erythroblastotic baby, according to Schwartz and Levine (1943). In the past these usually died and were an important source of wasted pregnancies. This no longer need be true.

The lower rate of 1 in 200 actually observed means that the genetic situation is overruled most of the time, a very fortunate state of affairs! It is not clear how in some of these cases the baby escapes the consequences of his genetics.

In case the baby does *not* escape his genetics and develops erythroblastosis, the following events are thought to have occurred.

The mother who is Rh negative never produces erythroblastotic children if her husband is likewise Rh negative. If he is Rh positive but carries the Rh negative gene, half of the children will be Rh negative and none of these will develop erythroblastosis. The other half will be Rh positive, just like the father, and are potentially victims of the disease. If both of the father's genes are Rh positive, then all the children will be Rh positive and potential victims. Thus, an Rh positive child carried by an

Rh negative mother is the setting for possible, though not inevitable, trouble.

If Rh positive red blood cells from the fetus are in the blood stream of an Rh negative mother she may produce antibodies against them. Usually she does not produce enough to become dangerous to her first child. But the antibodies may be augmented by the reaction to red blood cells from a second Rh positive fetus. The titer may rise to such a level that destruction of red blood cells within the body of the fetus commences and, if severe, produces erythroblastosis.

If the mother is Rh positive and her red blood cells invade the blood steam of an Rh negative fetus, one might expect the fetus to produce antibodies against the positive maternal antigens. However, the fetus is not highly successful in producing antibodies, in contrast to its capacity to produce antigens, and therefore this theoretic situation is not of practical importance, except on rare occasions.

While this sounds complicated, the genetic predictions and results are in satisfactory harmony. Harmony gives place to confusion when it comes to terminology. This is because it is at present impossible to decide just what the geography of the chromosome is like in the very restricted region concerned with the Rh factors. As there are at least three different antigens produced in certain individuals, one must assume either that one particular gene can produce all three at once or that there are three different gene loci close together in this region, each producing a single antigen. The former is the multiple allele theory supported by Wiener and the latter the linked multiple factor theory of Fisher. It doesn't make the slightest bit of difference which is correct as far as the management of the patient is concerned. The terminology does have to be different for the two hypotheses, and this results in the confusion. Both systems are well entrenched in the literature.

Table XIX gives the calculated frequencies of some of the most common Rhesus factor genotypes. There are many more alleles and combinations known, but it is not possible to give an exhaustive description of the Rhesus factors in this book. For an already somewhat out of date treatise on the blood groups of man, the reader is referred to the fourth edition of the definitive text by Race and Sanger (1962). It is impossible for them to keep their monograph up to date, and it is impossible for the physician to know every detail of the extremely complicated field of blood group genetics. He must be prompt to call upon blood bank or other blood group specialists for assistance in this highly technical area.

From the practical point of view, the most important reaction is that of the D antigen in the fetus causing antibody formation in Rh negative (*dd*) mothers. Occasionally an Rh positive mother can produce an erythroblastotic baby and catch her obstetrician off guard. This is called an *Hr* reaction and is usually the result of the production of antibodies by a *CC* mother against the *c* antigens in her *Cc* fetus. This is rare, but it can be disastrous. It warrants the small additional work of testing for all antibody titers possible to make sure that no baby is born with unsuspected erythroblastosis.

It was remarked earlier that many potential cases of

TABLE XIX   Frequencies of Some of the Main Rhesus Genotypes

Calculated Genotype Frequency, %	Genotype Symbols	
	Fisher	Wiener
15.1	cde/cde	rr
2.0	cDe/cde	R^0r
11.0	cDE/cde	R_2r
31.7	CDe/cde	R^1r
11.5	CDe/cDE	R^1R^2
16.6	CDe/CDe	R^1R^1

erythroblastosis are spared. The mother does not build up antibodies even though one would expect her to do so on genetic
grounds. An explanation of some of the fortunate exceptions to
genetic predictions was provided by Levine (1958). He found
that in some genotypes the A-B-O system protects against
erythroblastosis. His discovery was that Rh antibodies are produced more readily and to a higher titer in ABO-compatible matings than in ABO incompatibility. Stated the other way around,
ABO-incompatible matings sometimes give protection against
erythroblastosis. It is thought that Rh positive fetal red cells are
destroyed in the mother's vascular system, when they are ABO
incompatible, *before* they reach her sites of antibody production. Thus, they fail to initiate the antibody production that
would cause erythroblastosis. It has been calculated that the
chances for production of Rh antibodies are 2.4 times greater in
ABO-compatible matings than in ABO-incompatible matings.

Thus far, we have looked briefly at only one facet of blood
genetics. This is the most important one, from the routine genetic
counseling point of view. It is especially important because the
chances of serious damage to embryos conceived after antibody
build-up are higher than for the usual mendelian types of anomalies. It has been the writer's experience that when risks of serious
trouble exceed 25 per cent, parents are usually reluctant about
further pregnancies. With blood incompatibilities the chances of
trouble for each subsequent pregnancy may approach 50 per
cent or even 100 per cent, depending upon whether the husband
is heterozygous or homozygous for the gene involved. Fortunately, the affected babies can usually be salvaged today, but
many parents do not wish to experience this trauma, particularly if they already have a satisfying family. Few women think
of themselves as slot machines in which a chance is taken every
time something is inserted in the slot. They are not neutral about
their fertility. Either they want a baby or they do not. If they
want one, they want to be sure that it has a high chance of
being normal.

One of the many fascinating areas of blood genetics, for which we cannot give space in this book, is that of the hemoglobin abnormalities. The sickle cell–malaria interaction is one of the most basic and exciting sagas in all biology. An excellent small book on the hemoglobin abnormalities by Ingram (1961) is recommended for all those with even the slightest interest in this field.

Another area is that of the hemophilias. Most of these seem to be of the sex-linked recessive type, although a mild type reported by Bond et al. (1962) affects both males and females. The gene for this mild variety seems to be sex-linked also but is of at least intermediate dominance, which accounts for the affected females.

The genetics of the serum proteins is now receiving considerable attention. Many of the serum protein differences are relatively unimportant as counseling problems, but the agammaglobulinemia trait is sufficiently serious to give rise to counseling requests. Several genetic mechanisms, such as sex-linked recessive and dominant genes, seem to give rise to different abnormalities of the gamma globulins. The most recent monograph on the immunologic deficiency diseases is that of Good, Kelley, Rötstein and Varco (1962), which includes a bibliography of some 950 papers.

In summary, the major counseling problems on the American scene are those resulting from erythroblastosis due to ABO or Rhesus factor incompatibilities in which the mother produces antibodies against the antigens of her fetus and thereby may cause its death or damage. In some parts of the country counseling for sickle cell anemia and thalassemia may assume some importance, and pediatricians and obstetricians everywhere can expect questions about agammaglobulinemia. It is not possible to cover the wide range of topics on blood genetics in a small book. However, it is possible to emphasize the life and death aspects of the situation and to alert the physician to the need for further reading in the area. Fortunately, the genetic mechanisms involved are quite simple in their mendelian behavior. The person in charge of the blood laboratory can usually provide the physician with an adequate understanding of the consequences expected from the genotypes of the husband and wife concerned.

ILLUSTRATIVE EXAMPLES

1.   Various and frequent questions on the subject come in. Usually they concern Rhesus factors. This is natural, because the erythroblastic baby may be but the beginning of a chain of most serious events as the following case shows.

A most capable woman psychiatrist produced, as her only children, two erythroblastotic babies who did not survive. In spite of her understanding of mental illness, it was impossible for her to rid herself of the idea that she had murdered her own children. During the long treatment in a mental hospital that followed, she and her husband drifted apart and were divorced. She recovered eventually and is again a highly successful psychiatrist. Perhaps all this misery might have been prevented with the medical handling of erythroblastosis that is possible today. This woman came from a family with a history of mental illness, but there seems to be no question that the erythroblastosis disaster precipitated the mental disease.

2.   The writer has had personal expense and experience with this problem and found himself giving counsel to himself. The situation was the usual one of an Rh positive husband and Rh negative wife. The writer's wife had produced two Rh positive children without demonstrating any antibody formation. Three weeks before term of the third pregnancy, the antibodies appeared and the obstetrician considered it wise to bring about the birth of the baby at once, before erythroblastosis might set in. The question then arose of the prospects that a baby subsequent to the imminent one would develop erythroblastosis at such an early stage that damage to it would result before a cesarean section would be practical. Should another Rh positive embryo be produced, there might be serious trouble. An Rh negative child would be possible if the husband were heterozygous but not possible if he were homozygous Rh positive. An Rh negative

child would not be affected by the maternal antibodies. It was calculated that the chance that the next child would be Rh negative was 0.36. However, the chance of 0.64 that the child would be Rh positive, and therefore likely to be in serious trouble, was considered too large to trifle with. Consequently, at the same time that the baby was removed by cesarean section, the fallopian tubes of the mother were tied.

It was realized by both husband and wife that a salpingectomy is irreversible. However, the geneticist, of all people, should not knowingly take a large chance of producing a defective child. What is good for other families with problems due to heredity is good for the geneticist too.

The psychiatrist's son wets the bed,
The geneticist's son has Rh factors, instead!

Follow-up.
The operation worked. The couple have appreciated the efficiency of the operation and the freedom from the fear of pregnancy that it bestowed. Their only regret is that the uterus was not removed also to eliminate the nuisance of the menstrual cycle.

Chapter 19

DISPUTED PATERNITY

In 1945 a California jury decided that Charles Chaplin had fathered Joan Barry's daughter, Carol Ann. This decision cost Chaplin about $100,000 for attorney's fees, and he must provide a healthy sum each week to support Carol Ann until she is 21. The irony of it all is that Chaplin is not her father, unless by some strange chance one of Miss Barry's A blood group genes mutated to group B. This is unlikely.

Carol Ann has antigen B in her red blood cells. Her mother has blood group A and Chaplin, the "universal donor" type, has group O. The B antigen can be detected whenever present. In order for Carol Ann to have the gene for B antigen, she must have inherited it from her true father. As Chaplin does not have this gene, he could not have provided her with this antigen. By the laws of heredity he is excluded as a possible father, unless of course we accept the unlikely alternative that one of Miss Barry's germ cells had mutated from group A to group B. This would have removed the exclusion of Chaplin, and other blood groups could have been tested. As a betting proposition it would be safe to assume that Chaplin again would have been excluded from paternity. The M-N and Rhesus factors were known then and could have been used.

Illegitimacy is not a rare phenomenon. In some areas of

the United States at least 1 in 10 of the births is registered as illegitimate. This is less than the actual proportion, as these are only those from unmarried women and do not include the children from extramarital relations. It can be seen that there is a considerable opportunity here for service in determining the correct paternity.

There are two rules of thumb that are useful and to which exceptions can be expected only in the rare cases of mutation. These are:

1. The A and B antigens cannot appear in the blood of a child unless present in the blood of one of the parents.

2. A child of group O cannot come from a father or mother of group AB, and a child of group AB cannot have a parent of group O.

If we include other blood groups, the chances of excluding wrongly accused men at the fathers will increase. There are more than 10,000 possible different blood group combinations, which, if properly handled, go far toward the exclusion of a wrongfully accused individual from among the possible candidates for paternity. If large numbers of persons all had the same combinations of blood types, paternity determination would be impossible except in a small proportion of the cases. Actually the lack of identity of people selected at random for their blood types as a whole is quite remarkable. Bertinshaw, Lawler, Holt, Kirman and Race (1950) studied the blood groups of 475 persons and found the following:

211 blood group combinations occurred once only.
45 blood group combinations occurred twice.
17 blood group combinations occurred three times.
9 blood group combinations occurred four times.
7 blood group combinations occurred five times.

1 blood group combination occurred six times.
4 blood group combinations occurred seven times.
1 blood group combination occurred eight times.
1 blood group combination occurred ten times.

Thus, 211 (45 per cent) of the people had a blood group combination different from that found in any other person in the group of 475. Only one combination of blood groups occurred as often as 10 times. The blood group systems tested in order to obtain the above results are given below and, according to Dr. Race, give the accompanying percentages of failures to distinguish between two samples on the basis of each system *by itself*.

Rh	19% failures
MNS	20% failures
A_1A_2BO	33% failures
P	62% failures
Lewis	65% failures
Kell	82% failures
Lutheran	85% failures

The blood groups will probably continue to be the most powerful tool in the scientific determination of paternity by exclusion of men not in actuality the fathers of the children in question. The techniques work even better, of course, in cases of exchanged babies in hospitals. However, the latter are so rare as to be of little practical significance.

Scientifically, the routine for exclusion of particular individuals is well established. It should only take a short further period of research in human genetics to make the opposite routine feasible, that is, the determination that a particular person *is* the parent of a child. Only a slight shift in theory is necessary for such a consideration. In the case of allegation of positive paternity one still resorts to exclusion, in that one excludes everyone else in the population except the true father. The writer has done this only once, and then in a bizarre situation. This case will be considered as an illustrative example for this chapter. However, such positive determination of paternity is just around the corner and waits only for more research on the heredity of normal characteristics.

It should be mentioned that the blood groups are the best, but not the only useful, characteristics for the determination of paternity. It is possible to make use of physical characters of many kinds. Mohr reports a case in Norway in which the normal-handed mother of a brachyphalangic child designated a specific man as the father. The man denied his involvement but, when requested by the court to present his hands, turned out to be short fingered. He was adjudged by the court to be the father and forced to support the child. This decision was possible because the short fingers involved are caused by a rare dominant gene. The likelihood of any other man with this rare gene having been the father was too small to be worth consideration. As the father must have been heterozygous for this gene, because of its rareness, he had a 50 per cent chance of having a normal child. Had the child had normal fingers, the absence of brachyphalangy would not have absolved him from possible paternity and the case would have been back where it started.

In recent years there has been increased interest in establishing paternity for illegitimate children in Sweden and West Germany. It is only justice that the father of a child should make a financial contribution to its support. It is quite possible that the alarming illegitimacy rate in the United States would be cut significantly if it became known to the male population that paternity could be determined correctly and if there were laws requiring that tests be taken in disputed cases.

Beckman, Böök and Lander (1960) evaluated 25 of the anthropologic traits used in Swedish paternity tests. Only two of the traits did not appear to be inherited at all and would therefore be useless. The strength of heredity varied for the rest, and it would be best to discard the weakest ones as they tend to confuse rather than clarify. One good quantitative trait that can be used is total finger ridge count, which has a correlation of +0.43±0.08 between fathers and their children and is little influenced by environmental variations.

Friedrich Keiter, of the University of Würzburg, Hamburg, Germany, has worked on the problem of paternity tests and claims that he can discriminate between fathers and non-fathers in 95 per cent of cases. It is to be hoped that his methods will be made available for testing in America in the near future. I am willing to predict that paternity determinations will become important in this country as the taxpayers' revolt progresses. In the future, we will probably insist that all working males support their illegitimate children instead of leaving it up to the taxpayers in so many cases.

A relevant fact emphasized by the biochemist Roger Williams is that, with the 95 per cent level as the break between normal and abnormal variation in a quantitative trait, only 60 per cent (0.95^{10}) of the population would be normal for all of 10 traits, and only 0.59 per cent (0.95^{100}) would be normal for all 100 traits. Consequently, if sufficient genetic traits can be measured, paternity can be established beyond reasonable doubt. It should not be long before routine tables and directions are available for this purpose.

ILLUSTRATIVE EXAMPLES

1.   This is what seems to be a successful attempt to prove positive paternity, not for an illegitimate child, but for one born in wedlock in an ordinary family of better than average means. The boy was the third child. Shortly after his birth the father became obsessed with the idea that the baby was not his. He gradually extended his delusion to the point of disclaiming paternity of his two older children. He was sent to the University Hospitals and diagnosed as paranoid. He was later commited to a state hospital and received shock therapy. Upon discharge in a few months, he seemed no better. He still insisted that

at least the boy was not his, although in other social aspects he was
well adjusted and a good husband. The family physician had no
doubt as to the actual paternity and referred the three to the Dight
Institute. After blood tests were obtained from the Minneapolis War
Memorial Blood Bank, the genetic tests were made. The father passed
all these tests, in that he was not excluded on any one of them. This
is in itself pretty strong evidence for his paternity. But in order to
give a statistical expression for the chance that this man, and not any
other man picked at random, was the father, some calculations were
needed. These are given and explained, one by one, below.

		Mother	Father	Son
(a)	A-B-O group	A_1	A_2	A_1

This group is not of a diagnostic value because the child could
have had a father of any genotype except that homozygous for the
B gene, but such persons make up less than 1 per cent of the population and, furthermore, cannot be distinguished phenotypically from
those heterozygous for B.

		Mother	Father	Son
(b)	M-N types	MM	MN	MN

The frequency of men with MN and NN genotypes in the
population is about 75 per cent, and any of these could be assumed
to be the father at this step. The 25 per cent MM men can be
excluded.

		Mother	Father	Son
(c)	Rhesus factors	cde	CDe	CDe
		cde	cde	cde

All men testing for CDe could be assumed to be the father.
This phenotype is found in 52 per cent of the population. The proportion of men in the population with proper M-N and Rhesus factor
groups is thus 52 per cent of the 75 per cent; 39 percent are still
eligible as the possible father.

		Mother	Father	Son
(d)	Zygodactyly	Normal	Zygodactyly	Zygodactyly

At the old swimming hole the father had been referred to as
"frog feet" because of mild zygodactyly between the second and third
toes. The boy has the condition also. According to Basler (1926), as
many as 9 per cent of males have the condition. Consequently, only
9 per cent of the above 39 per cent of the population, that is, 3 per
cent, are still possible fathers of the boy. This is a valuable charac-

teristic and functions according to the same principle as brachyphalangy in the Norwegian case cited.

(e)	Eye color	*Mother* Hazel	*Father* Light brown	*Son* Blue

About one-third of the Minneapolis population has blue eyes.
According to the Hardy formula, about 18 per cent of the men would
be homozygous for dark eye pigment genes and could not have a
blue-eyed child. However, it is impossible to distinguish phenotypically this 18 per cent from the men who, like the father, have dark
eyes but carry the gene for blue eyes. As the determination of paternity would depend ordinarily on the appearance of the person and not
upon the genes he might carry, we cannot use the eye color as a diagnostic character. This was equally true for hair shape, hair color,
tongue curling, P.T.C. tasting, mid-digital hairs, ear lobe attachment,
and hair whorl. In all these cases the father could not be excluded
from paternity, nor could any part of the random population, because
of the impossibility of distinguishing those homozygous for the dominant gene from those heterozygous for it. But as this distinction can
be made with the various blood group systems, this part of the technique should be extended.

A summary of the situation is that the father has passed a long
series of tests, none of which excludes him from paternity of the boy.
In addition, all but 3 out of 100 men in the general population have
been excluded as eligible for paternity. It is not possible to combine
these two lines of evidence to give a statistical answer. However, the
use of judgment leaves no other conclusion but that this man is the
biologic as well as the legal father. But for the matter of mental illness, the case would never have come up.

Follow-up.
The father is an intelligent and well-read person. It was possible to explain the conclusions so that he understood how the chromosomes behave and what he should conclude from the tests. Neither
his wife nor the writer expected that this knowledge would help
much. A follow-up call to his wife at the time of writing revealed the
surprising information that he had recovered completely from his obsession and that everything was "just fine." Whether or not his education in genetics had anything to do with his recovery is, of course,
only an interesting speculation.

2.   The following situation involves a modern quirk concerning
expected paternity. A woman stated that her husband had proved to
be sterile, which was confirmed by biopsy. Semiadoption had been

arranged for, and three donors were to contribute sperm on three successive days. Two of the donors had blue eyes, but the third had brown eyes. The woman and her husband both have blue eyes and would expect all their children to have blue eyes, if it were possible for them to have children.

Request.

Suppose the child expected to result from the insemination has brown eyes, showing that the brown-eyed donor was the effective father. How do I explain the brown eyes to relatives and friends?

Reply.

You state that your husband's mother has brown eyes. If your listener, or interrogator, seems quite ignorant of genetics, you might suggest that the brown eyes came from the paternal grandmother. If this seems too flimsy an explanation, you might explain that the child displays a mutation from blue to brown eyes. If the questioner persists, you may have to imply that it is none of her business. A truthful statement of the situation would not seem to be indicated for the idly curious.

Chapter 20

SKIN COLOR

What have skin color and racial crosses to do with medical genetics? Nothing directly, though indirectly there is an important relationship. The physician working with the childless couple is often forced to give up any hope that a particular man and wife will produce their own children. Some physicians then drop the couple, thinking that their responsibility is at an end. Others may stay with the situation until they have gotten the couple on the "waiting list" of some adoption agency. But this may be a futile gesture, as plenty of people who get on a list are crossed off it after some months, because of the unavailability of newborn blue-ribbon babies. There are usually some older children available for adoption and also children with some percentage of African or Asian heredity. It is the opinion of the writer that these products of racial crosses are among the best adoption risks that there are. The reasons for this theory will be given later in the chapter.

Until the childless couple actually get a child, their needs have not been met. As there is such an acute shortage of children available for placement, the problem is an important and serious one, and the physician should be willing to give it careful attention both in his professional capacity and as an ordinary good citizen.

It is most remarkable that the largest single group of requests for information and counseling at the Dight Institute concerns the heredity of skin color. Most of the requests come from adoption agencies and concern the feasibility of placing for adoption children of mixed racial ancestry. The children are usually brought to the Dight Institute for an opinion as to their ability to "pass for white." The inevitable question is what the skin color and general features will be of the *offspring* of the children being considered. These children will marry into the white community if their placement is there. The potential foster parents are always perturbed about the old myth that a "black baby" is likely to appear from such a marriage. Such tales have been scientifically investigated a number of times and never have been found to have any basis in fact.

In all cases investigated where a person of mixed ancestry marries a white person, no child is ever darker than the mixed-ancestry parent, and the usual condition is that the offspring are intermediate between the parents in general appearance. This is in accord with genetic theory; were it *not* the case, we would be on the threshold of new discoveries the nature of which is quite unimaginable.

The problem of trying to decide whether a baby will be able to pass for white as an adult is not quite so simple as that of disposing of the "black baby" myth. Not enough research on the heredity of racial differences has been done to provide us with unequivocal answers. However, we must do the best we can with what we have. Problems affecting people today have to be solved today, and by following up our best guesses we can get some idea which of them were correct. Some diagnostic criteria for estimating whether a child can "pass for white" and thus enjoy the better socioeconomic conditions of the white community are given below.

THE SACRAL SPOT   This is a large blue area at the base of the spine which extends out onto the buttocks. It is present at birth but disappears within a few months or years. It is found in babies and young children of all the pigmented races and in many Caucasians with dark complexions. It probably is present in over 95 per cent of Negro children and in 1 per cent of French and Italian babies. It has never been seen in blond children with blue eyes. Consequently, if the spot is absent in the baby, it is evidence that no African genes for skin color are present.

FINGER SMUDGES   Babies with a little "colored blood" often show "smudges" of pigment on the backs of the fingers between the joints. While there may be no major gene for skin color present, occurrence of the smudges indicates that the child will develop a dark complexion. Absence of the smudges is a good indication that the skin color will be white and stay white.

SKIN COLOR   The baby should not be examined until at least six months of age because it will be lighter at birth than later on if skin color factors are present. If the child is to "pass for white," it is important that there be no major genes for skin pigmentation present, as the skin color seems to be the peg on which social discrimination hangs. A model study by Stern (1953) shows that there are four or five major pairs of genes concerned with the difference in skin color between Negroes and whites. Consequently, in the children who come to the Dight Institute for evaluation these few genes for Negro skin color are usually absent because ordinarily only about one-eighth of their heredity is Negro.

NOSE WIDTH   This is sometimes helpful, though somewhat deceptive because young babies have rather broad noses. The nose grows sharper and more pointed with age, so it can be assumed that with increased age the nose will tend to look less Negroid than at the time of inspection.

THICKNESS OF LIPS   In the children who are brought to

the Dight Institute for examination, the nose and lips usually are Caucasoid in appearance, or at least near enough to it so that they can pass for white.

EYE FOLD   Many Negroes have an epicanthal fold, and this seems to be inherited as a single dominant. It is often found in the children brought to the Dight Institute. If it is present, it decreases the likelihood that the child can "pass for white." On the other hand, when children with one gene for pigmentation are candidates for placement with oil-wealthy Indian families, the eye fold is an advantage. We have had a number of instances in which it was thought that the child might pass for an Indian.

HAIR SHAPE AND TEXTURE   One of the reasons why the child should not be evaluated before six months of age is that the permanent hair should be present for examination. None of the children whom we see have "kinky" hair, as the agencies realize that kinky or peppercorn hair would not pass. Some of the children do have extremely curly hair, and if it is also of very fine texture, it will "mat" badly in the back. Even so, it is thought that such children can pass for white if no other particularly Negroid features are present.

PIGMENTATION OF GENITALIA   If the genitalia are appreciably darker than the surrounding skin, Negro ancestry is evidenced.

If the child can pass for white, what are its chances of having good physical and mental characteristics, which would permit it to make a satisfactory adjustment in the foster home?

The number of bona fide orphans from good families, available for agency placement, is too small to be worth consideration. Therefore, if the couple go to an agency they should usually expect to get children who belong to one of the three categories below.

(1) LEGITIMATE CHILDREN FROM BROKEN HOMES   These children are likely to be from families where one or both parents were too feeble to maintain their children in the face of what seemed to them to be insuperable environmental difficulties. As there seems to be an appreciable risk that the children are likely to have genes for mental and physical deficiencies, the legitimate children would seem to be the poorest prospects for adoption.

(2) ILLEGITIMATE CHILDREN   The parents may be of poor genetic stock also, but there is a better chance that the children are the result of poor social conditions only and thus, if adopted as babies, would develop very satisfactorily. This category is always in great demand.

(3) CHILDREN OF MIXED RACIAL ANCESTRY   These babies are usually illegitimate and are usually the result of attractions between white persons and individuals with some Negro heredity. In many of these cases both parents are of considerable ability and the child is illegitimate because of social prejudice and pressure against a marriage that would have provided legitimacy. In many states such a marriage is prohibited by law. These children are probably the best genetic material available for adoption. Not only are the parents fundamentally more able than those in the two previous categories, but genetic weaknesses peculiar to one of the ancestral races might be covered up by strength in the other race.

The conclusion from these considerations is that the children from racial crosses are probably the most vigorous and healthy stock generally available for adoption. As there is little demand for them, the supply is good. If potential foster parents are found to be free of racial prejudices and also match the children to some extent in appearance, the placement can be expected to be highly successful. That has been the experience from the follow-up of children seen at the Dight Institute. For details of the follow-up of children of mixed racial ancestry, see

Reed and Nordlie (1961). It should be emphasized that the parents must be informed of the presence of a dash of "colored blood," and it must be clear that they are capable of accepting the fact without emotion before the child is placed with them.

ILLUSTRATIVE EXAMPLES

1.   *Request.*
      A pair of male fraternal twins, eight months old, with some Negro heredity, were to be placed for adoption. A white family was interested in adopting them if it was thought that they would fit into the community and that their offspring would do likewise. Since it is more difficult to place boys than girls, and Negro than white children in white families, the welfare board was particularly interested in a prediction.

      Reply.
      Upon examination both boys appeared to be free of skin pigmentation, had blue eyes and blond hair in ringlets. There was some slight evidence of Negro ancestry in the features of the nose and mouth. One boy was "lighter" in appearance than the other. Both could undoubtedly pass for white and immediate placement in the interested family would have been indicated except for the fact that the "lighter" boy gave some evidence of a neural lesion. He had nystagmus and still had some trouble in controlling his head movements. It was recommended that placement be postponed until his nervous condition had been clarified by further medical attention.

2.   *Request.*
      Sixteen years ago I adopted a little girl from an orphanage. The mother was unmarried, and she told the Sister in charge of the orphanage that the father was white. The girl has now grown up to be a nice young lady, and we love her very much. The only thing that puzzled us was her hair because it is always real dry and kinky like Negroes' hair. It got to a point where the children in school would call her "nigger" and it made her very sad. You see, she does not know she is adopted as yet. My curiosity got the best of me, and I went back to the orphanage and had the Sister check on the girl's father. It turned out that he was a mulatto.

      Now my worry is, will she be able to marry and have white children or is there a possibility of her children being colored? We love our daughter very much and would hate to see her hurt later on. This has upset me very much, and I don't know what to do.

Reply.

Evidently your girl's only major Negro characteristic is kinky hair. This behaves as a dominant trait and would be passed on to half of your daughter's children. This 50 per cent chance that each of her children would have kinky hair is a statistical concept. In her particular family all, or none, or any combination of the children might have kinky hair. If the husband's hair is straight, the kinky hair in the children might be less pronounced and be manageable as tight curls. Kinky hair occurs in some families where there has been no Negro ancestry.

Your daughter will marry a white man, no doubt, and we can assure you that her children won't look any more Negroid than she does, as her Negro heredity will be reduced by one-half in her children.

It is a pity that the agency that placed your daughter with you was not more careful in evaluating the child before adoption. You could have then decided whether or not you wished to risk the perplexing situation, which it is now impossible for you to avoid.

3.   The following is a most unusual case in which the writer was requested by the court to testify as an expert witness.

A young woman lived off and on with a man of about 60 years of age. The man had approximately one-fourth Negro heredity. She was white and promiscuous, having served time in the workhouse after having been arrested in a different kind of house. She became pregnant, and the part-Negro man married her about six weeks before the boy was born. He thus became the legal father of the boy. The mother was not interested in the more routine aspects of housekeeping and soon abandoned her husband and the baby. It was adjudicated that she had abandoned and neglected the child but that the man had *not* done so. In fact, he had kept the child clean and in good health. However, the county welfare board opined that every child should have a mother, that the man was too old to be a good parent in future years, that superficially it looked as if he were *not* the biologic father of the child, and therefore, that his legal parenthood should be set aside. The welfare board petitioned for permanent custody with the intention of placing the child for adoption. The court requested an opinion from the Dight Institute as to whether or not the man was the biologic father of the child.

The "father" had at least one gene for skin color and dark brown hair, which was kinky. He could never pass for white. The boy could never pass for Negro. He had ash blond hair, blue eyes, no skin pigmentation and a very fair complexion. His hair was straight, coarse and rather unruly. The total picture showed no resemblances between the boy and the "father" except that both had blue eyes. It was the opinion of the writer that the man was not the father of the boy, who was typically Scandinavian in appearance. However, the writer suggested that blood tests be given as a more scientific way of answering the paternity question. The court requested the blood tests. The phenotypes for the groups tested are given below.

			BLOOD GROUPS			
	A-B-O	*Rhesus*	*M-N*	*Kell*	*Duffy*	*Lewis*
"Father"	B	CDe	MN	kk	Fy^a	Le(a$^-$)
Boy	A$_2$	CDe	MM	kk	Fy^a	Le(a$^-$)
Mother	A$_2$	CDe	MN	kk	Fy^a	Le(a$^-$)

It can be seen from the above that all three persons have different genotypes, but unfortunately, from the point of view of the county, the man is not excluded as the father. Considering the first three sets of blood groups only, there is still about a 75 per cent chance that some other man was the father, as only A$_1$A$_1$, BB and NN men (25 per cent of the male population) and a few rare Rhesus types are excluded as possible fathers. The last three blood groups are too common to exclude any appreciable proportion of the population as possible fathers of the boy.

Chapter 21

STRING BEANS AND CHUBBIES

Every mother is greatly concerned with the administration of food to her baby. Many a baby has gotten off to a rough start because the pediatrician insisted that the mother nurse the child even though she had insufficient milk. Thanks to their genetics, most babies suffer no permanent physical damage as a result of the short period of semistarvation before the mother's milk finally dries up completely. They soon catch up with the contented bottle-fed babies.

After the hassle with the bottles ends, we find mothers worrying about the amount and types of food that the child consumes. There is no evidence whatever that this flutter of anxiety about the feeding of the child does it any good. It may well be that concern of the parents about the child's eating habits, other than that of supplying vitamins and adequate amounts of food, leads to nothing but behavior problems and later neuroticism. If parents only understood that the child's eventual body size and shape will agree with its heredity to a large degree, they would relax and let nature take its course with satisfactory results. Unless they can definitely guide their children's eating habits without the development of psychologic tensions, it would be better to ignore the problem completely. This does not mean that the children should be fed off the floor; it merely means that eating should be considered to be a normal process and not a continuous mental crisis.

Overeating and undereating are psychologic weapons, which even the youngest children use on their parents if they show concern about eating habits. The child merely accentuates his tendencies to overeat or undereat for what seems to him to be profitable concessions forced from his parents.

What does heredity have to do with body size and shape? The Greeks were interested in the subject and realized that there were different body types and had names for them. Kretschmer classified the body types as pycnic, athletic and leptosomic. The first extensive family studies of body size and shape were by Davenport (1923). He described his types as very fleshy, fleshy, medium, slender and very slender. His work shows clearly that when both parents are slender, the children are slender in the majority of cases. When both parents are fleshy, they have children showing a much greater variability of types from very slender to very fleshy. The material is adequate to show that more than 3, and perhaps less than 10, pairs of genes provide the major hereditary variation in body size. The genes causing slender body type seem to show some recessiveness to those for fleshy body types, and slender children segregate out in the progeny from fleshy parents more frequently than do fleshy children from slender parents.

It is reasonable to assume that body build is correlated with eating habits, or vice versa. The point of interest to the physician is whether a person's eating habits are imposed upon him by his mother or whether the person makes an independent selection from the food available. If the person's eating habits are imposed by the mother, who even today still usually selects and prepares the food, the person's body build should resemble that of the mother more than that of the father. If, however, the person selects his food from that available, and children are obviously very selective, the body build should be a result of the person's genotype and about intermediate between that of the father and the mother.

This question can be settled by an analysis of Davenport's data. He used an index of weight in pounds divided by stature in inches squared, all multiplied by 1,000. This gives a series of index numbers for individuals, running from 20 for the very slender to 60 and over for the very fleshy. While the index is at fault in that it does not distinguish between weight due to fat and that due to muscle, it is entirely adequate for use in answering the question of whether eating habits come from within the person (his genotype) or result from the tastes of the mother. The sons and daughters of Davenport's study were postadolescent, and adjustments were made for the age differences of the parents and progeny.

The writer has Davenport's original data at the Dight Institute and has done a little piece of research on them to be presented here. A selection was made of all the cases in which there was a difference of 3 or more index points between the mother and the father in body build. The data were then divided into two groups, one in which the mother was fleshier than the father and the other the reciprocal. The results are shown in Table XX.

It is clear that the body builds of the children are precisely intermediate, on the average, between those of the parents. This would be expected if body size were determined by the genotype of the person rather than by the food preferences of the mother. The children succeed in selecting what they wish to eat from the offerings provided by the mother.

A correlated point comes from a study by Keys et al. (1950), showing that in normal people the cholesterol level in

TABLE XX   A Demonstration That the Body
Build of the Progeny, as Measured by Davenport's
Index, is Intermediate Between That of the Parents (Average Indices for 380 Pairs of Parents and
Their 1,267 Children)

	Mother Thinner than Father	Mother Fleshier than Father
Average index of mothers	30.4	40.2
Average index of fathers	38.4	32.8
Average index of parents	34.4	36.5
Average index of daughters	33.7	35.4
Average index of sons	35.6	36.3
Average index of progeny	34.7	36.0

the blood is determined by the constitution of the person and not
by his diet. The exception to this is that the cholesterol blood
level will decrease sharply on a completely cholesterol-free diet
rigidly observed. But let us be realistic about it: completely cholesterol-free diets exist only under laboratory conditions. Halfway measures have no effect, and it makes no difference who does
your cooking for you.

All this sounds like sheer fatalism. Actually, it is an attempt to focus attention on the fact that parents who try to control their children's diets in an arbitrary fashion may end up with
psychologic messes for children who are about the same sizes and
shapes that they would have been without the fights over eating
habits.

Since Davenport's work, considerable progress has been
made in the classification of body sizes and shapes. Sheldon
(1954) has developed a numerical scale that describes the body
build, or "somatotype," of the person. This system considers the
body from the point of view of the relative development of the
three embryonic layers from which it comes. These layers are the
endoderm, which gives rise to the viscera; the mesoderm, which

becomes bone and muscle; and the ectoderm, whence come the skin and nervous system.

Persons whose digestive systems are noticeably well developed and who are fat with well-rounded faces and "ham-shaped" arms and legs are the "chubbies" and are termed *endomorphs*. The endomorphs are alleged to have a relaxed and jovial temperament. Everybody loves a fat man!

The development of the second embryonic component, the mesoderm, provides the muscles and bones necessary for masculine glory. The bone and muscle men are called *mesomorphs*. Such persons do not mind flexing their muscles in public and make good salesmen and executives. You've got to be a football hero to get along with the beautiful girls—at least while still at school!

The last category of people are the *ectomorphs,* the "string beans." They are deficient in fat and muscle. As athletic success is not possible for the ectomorph of 18 years of age who is 68 inches tall and weighs 108 pounds, he turns to such intellectual pursuits as entomology or genetics. He is apt to become a professor.

The ectomorph was described in a humorous vein by the late Professor Hooton. His poem is reproduced here with his permission and that of the *Harvard Crimson,* where it was first published.

THE ECTOMORPH

BY EARNEST A. HOOTON

✿   ✿   ✿   ✿

A WARNING AGAINST TALL, THIN MEN

Girls, if you ever contemplate
A gamble on the married state,

Beware an ectomorphic mate.
That dolichocephalic head
Denotes a guy you should not wed.

Those lantern jaws and cranelike necks,
Kyphotic spines, shoulders convex,
Imply an appetite for sex
That makes wives into nervous wrecks.

Long, bony shanks and flat behinds
Oft go with introverted minds;
The man who has a pinched-in-belly
Is no more stable than a jelly.

Those elongated, thready muscles
Bespeak for you incessant tussles
When you wish to step out at night
With this cerebrotonic blight.

He pesters you with his embraces
When you want to be going places,
But, at the time for such caresses
He gets up out of bed and dresses,
Reads philosophical abstractions,
Oblivious of your attractions.
And when he does turn out the light,
He thrashes through a restless night.

Before his breakfast he is savage
Because his peptic ulcers ravage
Both his gut and his temperament,
Making him mean and flatulent.

Measles, bronchitis, whooping-cough
Were once enough to carry off
Each fragile ectomorphic brat
That any luckless pair begat.

But now that pediatrics works,
The world is full of brainy jerks
Inventing atom bombs and such,
And reproducing all too much.

To return to Sheldon's work on the somatotypes. The
beauty of his system is that by giving numerical grades of from

1 to 7 for each of the three basic components a value can be obtained, such as 2–3–5 or 4–4–3 or 1–1–7, which gives a clear picture of the body build of the person. Studies of the heredity of body build should now be made, scoring the parents and children according to their numerical somatotype. It would be a tremendous job to get sufficient families in which the parents had the somatotypes one wanted to observe, with sufficient offspring, but it could and should be done.

An immediate practical use of a rough kind of somatotyping is known as the Wetzel Grid. The pediatrician plots the weight/height index of the child on the Wetzel Grid. If the child's plot stays within the appropriate channel on the grid, then all is well. If he departs from the channel, the pediatrician should search for organic or psychologic problems. Wolanski (1961) has presented a new graphic method for evaluating the tempo and harmony of physical growth of children.

The reader may have gotten the idea that this subject is primarily useful for parlor games. Such is far from the case. The proportion of thin people who never marry is much higher than that of fat people, for example. The relationships of somatotypes to different illnesses is highly significant and of great importance. Everyone should have a lively interest in body build, and practically everyone does. It is a fascinating subject and it is appropriate to recommend the small book by Parnell (1958) as an introduction to this exciting discipline.

ILLUSTRATIVE EXAMPLES

1.   *Request.*
        Mr. J. was referred to the Dight Institute by an adoption agency. Mr. J. and his wife had requested the privilege of adopting a baby. The agency had refused to consider their request because the couple had not tried to produce children of their own. The reason the

couple preferred to adopt children was Mr. J.'s extreme sensitiveness about his height of 6 feet, 7 inches. He cannot buy ready-made clothes, he doesn't fit into Pullman berths, and life is exasperating because our culture is not cut according to his size. Mr. J.'s parents were both over 6 feet tall, as are all his sibs; he is the tallest and most uncomfortable of all the family.

Reply.

It was pointed out that as his wife is not over average height and more than one pair of genes is concerned with height, his children would not be expected to equal his height. Both the genetic and environmental contributions to height were explained to his satisfaction. He was both pleased and surprised at the unfoldings of science and left the office intent on reproduction!

Follow-up.

The writer contacted Mr. J. many years later. He had neither produced nor adopted any children. However, he had solved his various mental conflicts by taking charge of the child of a relative. Apparently this solution was satisfactory to all concerned.

2.   *Request.*

The third child of a normal couple turned out to be an achondroplastic dwarf. The couple were much perturbed and wondered whether they both carried heredity for this type of dwarfism and what chance there was that any subsequent children of theirs would be affected.

Reply.

The achondroplastic type of dwarfism is not a recessive and therefore could not be concealed by either parent. It is a dominant, and if the affected boy should have offspring, half of them would be expected to be dwarfs. You might ask how it was possible that neither of the boy's parents showed the trait if the heredity is dominant. The answer was worked out in Denmark, where it was found that in cases like this the affected child represents a new "mutation" from the normal gene to the gene for achondroplasia in the reproductive organs of one or the other of the parents. As this mutation, or change, in the gene probably occurred in only a small sector of the ovary or testis of the parent, it is unlikely that subsequent sibs of the boy would be abnormal.

3.   A sailor writes: "I would appreciate it if you could help me on a very serious problem.

Request.

"It seems that my mother-in-law had a beautiful figure up

until the time my wife was born. From then on she proceeded to get very fat. She says she watched her diet, but the doctors told her that all her troubles were glandular. At the present time she weighs about 210 pounds and is only about 5'1" tall. She and my wife are both about the same height.

"My mother-in-law has frightened my wife into thinking that if she has any children, she'll get very fat too. She says the whole trouble is glandular and there is nothing you can do about it, as it has always run in the family.

"I sincerely hope you can give me an answer on this problem, as we both want children but hate to have her lose her figure."

Reply.

Fat comes from food only. If she cuts down on the food supply, then the fat will take care of itself. Women do gain weight during pregnancy, but with a diet suggested by her physician and with post-pregnancy exercises, which he will describe, your wife can have a figure and children, too. Sometimes it takes a lot of will power, but it can be done! Good luck.

Chapter 22

HEART DISEASES

This chapter and the following one are a little ridiculous from a genetic point of view, in that they cover all sorts of genetically independent and unrelated abnormalities under a single heading. We get requests such as "What is the genetics of heart disease?" and "Tell me all about cancer."

Heart diseases are the most common cause of death, but except for congenital heart defects, we get few counseling requests concerning coronary and other heart diseases of adults. Perhaps the lack of anxiety here is due to the realization that most patients have completed their reproduction. Perhaps heart diseases of the aged are considered to be a relative blessing. We must all die sometime, and coronary heart disease is preferable to cancer. This attitude is neatly expressed by the jingle written by Mrs. Irwin Diamond:

> We all have to go, Dr. Keys,
> But the guy with the "heart" goes with ease.
> So why give up butter and cheese
> And wait for some ghastly disease?

The present interest in Dr. Keys results from his crusade to reduce the saturated fats in the diet, with the expectation that the serum cholesterol level will be lowered and deaths from heart diseases reduced. It is not clear that dietary control is a practical solution to the problem. If the difficulties of overcoming one's genotype by dietary manipulations are too great, his program will have little effect upon our vital statistics. Unfortunately, we do not know how strong the control of the genotype may be. Thomas (1959) studied the familial patterns in hypertension and coronary heart disease. She found that three times as many young, healthy medical students with hypercholesteremia had a parent affected by coronary atherosclerosis as did matched subjects with more normal values. One might also refer to the paper by Cruz-Coke (1959) on the hereditary factor in hypertension.

Let us leave this cheery controversy and consider the group of defects for which there is considerable counseling demand, the congenital heart diseases.

There have been many estimates of the incidence of congenital heart disease, most of which are too low because of difficulties of ascertainment. The team of physicians and others of the Department of Social Medicine (not to be confused with socialist medicine) at the University of Birmingham, England, has done a remarkable job in determining the frequency of many anomalies for the entire population of that large city. Complete samples for only one city are usually much more valuable than small random samples from various localities.

The excellent data on congenital heart diseases in Birmingham for the years 1940 to 1949 were published by Mac-Mahon, McKeown and Record (1953). The average incidence for these years was 3.2 per 1,000 total births. There is a high mortality, particularly during the first month, at the end of which the frequency had dropped to 2.1 per 1,000 children, while at the end of 10 years it is about 1.1 per 1,000 children. Thus, in the past, two-thirds of those born with congenital heart diseases failed to survive until 10 years of age. Polani and Campbell (1960) think that the incidence of congenital heart diseases is closer to 6.0 per 1,000. Careful examinations of babies at birth will probably substantiate the higher figure.

The only anomaly found to be significantly associated with the congenital heart cases was mongolism, or Down's syndrome, which was present in 6 per cent of them. The association is, of course, the other way around, the congenital heart defects being a part of Down's syndrome, which results from trisomy of the 21st pair of chromosomes.

There are a number of records of families in which more than one person in the family had congenital heart disease. These multiple cases could be evidence of common heredity, common environment or coincidence. McKeown, MacMahon and Parsons (1953) have studied the parents, brothers, sisters and first cousins of the 425 propositi with congenital heart disease discovered in the Birmingham studies cited before. In these families there were 342 sibs born subsequent to the propositi, of whom 6 had congenital heart defects. This is an incidence of 17.5 per 1,000, or about six times that (3.2 per 1,000) in the general population of births. The incidence in cousins and parents was not significantly greater than would be expected for the general population. There were only two cases of first cousin marriages and one of second cousins among the 424 marriages of parents of propositi. Thus, there was no increase in consanguinity over that expected for the general population.

The main conclusion from the study of McKeown, MacMahon and Parsons (1953) is that there is a significant excess of cases of congenital heart disease among the brothers and sisters of the original cases. The absence of excessive consanguinity is not helpful in trying to determine the influence of heredity for common abnormalities such as congenital heart malformation. The risk of a second case in the sibship is 1.8 per cent, a most helpful figure for counseling work. We see that there is an increased risk in the sibship, but whether this is due to heredity or common environment has to be determined by some other technique, such as a twin study.

Anderson (1954) has made an obvious, but essential, advance in the study of juvenile heart disease. He selected a series of cases all with the same defect, patent ductus arteriosus. It was possible to secure complete family data for 117 cases. Of these, 105 represented cases of uncomplicated patent ductus, 4 gave a history of maternal rubella and 8 had an additional cardiac defect. The 105 cases had a total of 145 later-born siblings, of whom 2 had patent ductus, a risk figure of 1.4 per cent. This is about five times the expectation for random appearance.

Of Anderson's 105 cases, 4 were members of twin pairs. These twin pairs were all discordant (only one member affected) and included one set of identical twin girls, one set of identical twin boys (blood tests) and two sets of probably identical twin girls. One of the later-born affected siblings was a member of a set of probably nonidentical twin girls. While a few sets of concordant identical twins with congenital heart disease have been reported, the total information on twins not only is scanty, but what there is fails to give much hint of any hereditary basis for these malformations. While, as always, it would be unwise to rule heredity out, it is certainly of rather minor importance here.

There is a clear-cut physiologic relationship between the sex of the individual and the expression of the patent ductus arteriosus. In Anderson's complete series of cases there were only 54 (26 per cent) affected males to 151 (74 per cent) affected females.

Anderson also found some suggestion of a seasonal influence upon the appearance of patent ductus. He agreed with previous workers that cases associated with maternal rubella are born in the late months of the year. The data on cases associated with additional cardiac defects are striking in showing a high incidence in the winter months.

As a result of his work and that of others, Anderson thought that patent ductus arteriosus should not be considered an entity of single etiology. There would appear to be at least three separate groups: (1) uncomplicated cases, (2) cases associated with maternal rubella and (3) cases associated with additional cardiac defects but with no history of rubella. If this be so, it is all the more reason that the whole field of congenital heart malformations be divided according to the obviously different defects for separate treatment in future studies.

Since Anderson's paper a number of such more specific studies have been done. One of the more recent is that of Polani and Campbell (1960), who analyzed as best they could the factors in the causation of persistent ductus arteriosus. The incidence of congenital heart disease among the sibs of their patients was 2.1 per cent, which is in agreement with Anderson's finding and greatly exceeds the expectation for the general population. It is always noted that there is no excess of affected parents of the patients. This must be the case with any trait that in the last generation was often lethal. Such persons did not survive to become parents.

The importance of chromosome studies has been emphasized in an early chapter of this book. Malformations of the heart have been a frequent feature of the "chromosomal" syndromes, such as Down's syndrome. Therefore, further attention must be paid to the portion of heart defects resulting from chromosomal aberrations. An interesting study of this sort is that of Böök, Santesson and Zetterqvist (1961). They studied the chromosomes of two members of a pedigree with eight certain and five probable cases of atrial septal defect of the secundum type. The two affected members studied both had an extra chromosome of the 19 to 20 group. They planned to study more

of the affected relatives, and it is possible that these will be found
to have this small extra chromosome.

ILLUSTRATIVE EXAMPLE

Request.

A physician is concerned about his patient who has had two
babies, both of whom had congenital heart defects, which resulted
in the death of one infant and an interventricular defect in the second. The patient is expecting a third baby in July. She would like to
know the likelihood of having another baby with a congenital heart
defect. No members of her family nor her husband's family have had
congenital heart defects.

Reply.

Evidence collected in England and at our heart clinic indicates
that once a baby has been born with congenital heart disease, the
likelihood of a later child having it is about 1 chance in 50. We do
not have data that would give the risk after the birth of two affected
infants. I think we can define the limit as being greater than 1 in 50
and less than 1 in 4. Perhaps a good estimate would be 1 in 20
where the mother has already had two children with congenital heart
disease. Usually there is about a 50–50 chance that a second defect
will be similar to the first one (that is, both interventricular defects,
both patent ductus, etc.). Incidentally, there is no increased risk for
having noncardiac malformations. In other words, there is a rather
"pure" familial tendency to congenital heart disease. You probably
have read about the recent surgery on interventricular defects at the
University of Minnesota; one of the three cases mentioned also had a
sister with interventricular defect.

The incidence of congenital heart disease among all infants is
about 1 in 250, so you see that the risk for this mother increased
about tenfold.

Follow-up.

The mother was delivered of a perfectly normal child according to schedule.

Chapter 23

CANCERS

M any persons wondered why the first edition of this book did not contain a chapter on the genetics of neoplasms. There were two reasons. Cancers are usually found in adults, and we get few counseling cases as a result. Even though our book on the biologic variables related to human breast cancer (Anderson, Goodman and Reed, 1958) is favorably known around Minnesota, we hardly ever get counseling requests concerned with breast cancers. The second reason is that a first draft of a chapter on cancers was written but discarded. I do not like the present chapter either, as it is next to impossible to cover such a large subject in a necessarily short chapter. However, a few comments may show why the subject is so difficult to handle adequately.

A cancer is a clone of cells growing without normal morphogenetic controls in a living host. Its etiology can be approached through radiology, biochemistry, endocrinology, immunology and, particularly, genetics. With our general knowledge of gene control over physiology and growth, it is inconceivable that any type of cancer would not in some way be influenced by genes. Accordingly, it is not surprising that when neoplasms have been studied in mice and other organisms, the influence of genetic factors is always found. In man, the difficulty arises because for common cancers we also always expect and find important environmental factors involved in their onset. Disentangling the genetic and environmental factors becomes the more difficult with the greater frequency of the trait. Some resolution can be obtained for breast cancer or pulmonary tumors in mice, but with man the technical difficulties are greater, although the general principles should be the same.

It is important to note that in the mouse, in which the genetics of cancer has been most thoroughly and satisfactorily studied, no tumor has been shown to be influenced by only a single gene. Instead, multiple-factor inheritance prevails. It is remarkable that Heston and his associates (1961) have demonstrated an association between eight identified genes on six different chromosomes and the frequency of pulmonary tumors. These genes include traits such as absence of hair, lethal yellow and fused tail.

We do know of some single genes in man that cause tumors. Some of the classic cases are neurofibromatosis, retinoblastoma and Gardner's syndrome. All three behave as relatively good mendelian dominants. All three result from independent mutations that survive for relatively few generations before becoming extinct in each family line. New mutations in other families maintain the characteristic frequencies of the three unrelated types of tumors in the world population. Naturally, all three are rare in the population, as they are often lethal, and their frequencies are intimately related to their mutation rates, which are of the order of 1 mutation in every 100,000 to 1,000,000 people.

Common traits, such as breast cancer, which may cause considerable decrease in the production of children, cannot become frequent in the population unless the primary genes concerned are modified by secondary genes or environmental factors. Thus, we do not expect to find breast cancer dependent for its expression upon a single clear-cut mendelian dominant or recessive gene. When we do not get clear-cut mendelian pedigrees for a trait, our interest in the genetic background may begin to wander and some may abandon the genetic concept completely. Nonetheless, every trait is always the result of the interaction of heredity and environment.

One of the havens for the refugees from genetics has been the cancer virus. One of the first of these "viruses" was the mammary tumor agent. It was discovered by Bittner, a geneticist using genetic techniques. Furthermore, he showed clearly that the propagation and transmission of the agent was under the influence of the genes of the host. The genetics of the virus must be considered as well as the genetics of the host. Blair (1960) demonstrated a clear-cut mutation in the mammary tumor agent. The mutant virus did not increase the incidence of tumors, but it did cause them to appear at a significantly earlier age. Fortunately, much of the controversy over the relative roles of genes and viruses has disappeared as the close relationships of the two have become apparent.

We can be sure that the common cancers in human beings depend upon no single etiologic agent for their development. The genetics of the host must be of importance in many ways and many different genes must be involved. Therefore, we can predict that genetic studies of the close relatives of breast cancer patients might show increased susceptibility to breast cancers but not necessarily any excess of other types of cancers. This has been abundantly confirmed by different groups of workers.

Anderson, Goodman and Reed (1958) showed adequately that relatives of breast cancer patients do not have an excess of cancers at other sites. Our work, in combination with that of many others, shows that mothers, sisters and daughters of breast cancer patients have about twice as much breast cancer as the control relatives. In crudest terms, the likelihood of a female relative of the first degree of relationship developing a breast cancer by age 85 is about 10 per cent; for the appropriate control females it is 6 per cent. Actually, the chances are much lower than this for any counseling client because few live to be 85 years of age.

Likewise, Woolf (1955) found about twice as many carcinomas of the stomach in the first-degree relatives of his proposit as were present in the control relatives. Empiric risk figures for counseling are about the same as for breast cancers. In terms of actual deaths from stomach cancer, the figures are 2.7 per cent mortality and 1.5 per cent mortality in the control relatives.

Some exciting new approaches to at least the fringes of an understanding of cancers come from perhaps unexpected quarters. The break-through came when Aird, Bentall and Roberts (1953) found that patients with gastric carcinoma have a higher frequency of blood group A than do corresponding control individuals. It should be stated that the differences are small, but they are based on tremendous numbers of tests from cities throughout the world. The consistency of the findings everywhere is strong evidence for their reality.

It is not known why this small excess of associations between stomach cancer and blood group A exists. At the moment this fact is of no practical use but it is most helpful to have theoretic springboards of this kind from which to take off in search of better explanations for the onset of cancers than we now have. Other cancer–blood group associations are less reliably established. For a good review of the subject, Chapter 4 by Clarke (1961) in *Progress in Medical Genetics* is recommended.

In summary, we expect to get counseling requests regarding the rare types of neoplasms, such as neurofibromatosis and retinoblastoma. If the affected child represents a new mutation, there is only a small chance of his having an affected sibling. It is impossible to predict how small this chance is because there is no way of knowing what percentage of the gonad tissue of the parent bears the mutated gene. The affected child can expect that somewhere between 25 and 50 per cent of his children will be affected, as expected for a dominant gene, with the factors of age of onset and penetrance making their usual contributions to variability. We do not expect many counseling requests regarding the common cancers. The chance of a patient having affected children of siblings is about double that of appropriate controls, but it is still only in the neighborhood of about 2 to 3 per cent. Counseling loses much of its utility for common traits where the risk of repetition is this low.

ILLUSTRATIVE EXAMPLE

Request.

Friends of the writer have a son who had one eye enucleated because of retinoblastoma and several years later lost the other eye. Probably the early years with vision were helpful in the subsequent period of adjustment, because the boy has done extremely well in school. A basic superior intelligence will permit the young man to solve life's problems better than many persons with perfect vision but less insight. Recently he fell in love, which brought up the problem of reproduction for future solution.

Reply.

Retinoblastoma in this case is certainly due to a new mutation in one of the boy's parents or to his being a phenocopy. The fact that his retinoblastoma was eventually bilateral would seem to make the phenocopy idea a weak reed upon which to pin one's hopes. Thus the chance for each of his children to be also affected would seem to be from 25 to 50 per cent. If an affected child were produced, reproduction would certainly be discontinued. The still unanswered question is whether any reproduction would be appropriate in these otherwise rather favorable circumstances.

Chapter 24

CONVULSIVE SEIZURES

Inquiries about convulsive seizures are second in number to those about skin color. The social stigma associated with convulsive seizures is greater than for any other disease that has come to our attention. The disease is a matter of great concern to the patient and his relatives. The secrecy involved is well illustrated by the disclosure that Emilie Dionne, one of the famous identical quintuplets, had suffered seizures from the age of three until her death on August 6, 1954. It seems remarkable that the seizures had been concealed from the public for 17 years, when they occurred in a person of such international conspicuousness.

For practical purposes, one might consider that convulsive seizures result from recurring excessive neuronal discharges within the central nervous system. In other mammals, such as the rabbit, simple recessive heredity for seizures has been demonstrated in specific strains of animals. This might well be the case in particular families of men. The difficulty results from our desire to have a single set of rules for convulsive seizures in all families taken as a group. It is unlikely that a single type of heredity is the basis for all the types of seizures. Consequently, our counseling in this field is scientifically of poor quality, although in spite of that it can be of great value to the peace of mind of the client. Because of the social stigma involved, the relatives and patients expect the chances of a repetition of the disease to be much higher than they actually are.

Symptomatic seizures are those resulting from trauma or organic disease of the brain, such as cerebral tumor. Idiopathic seizures are those cases where no cause (other than heredity) can be found for them. Naturally, we will not be concerned here with the symptomatic or strictly environmental cases but with the idiopathic types, where some hereditary basis for the seizures is probably present.

Convulsive seizures of all types are very frequent, about 1 person in every 250 being affected. The disease is often accompanied by mental deficiency or vice versa. It is not clear what the connection between mental deficiency and seizures is, but it may be partly due to the inferior social position of the epileptic, which would tend to restrict his choice of mates to genetic stocks of low mental capacity, as indicated by Kallmann and Sander (1947) in some cases.

We look to the twin material, as usual, for evidence of heredity for convulsive seizures. The largest series of twins at least one of whom had convulsive seizures was reported by Conrad (1940). The uncorrected concordance rates are 66.6 per cent for the identical twins and only 3.1 per cent for the fraternals as shown below. The morbidity rate for monozygotic cotwins increased to 86.3 per cent when only clinically "idiopathic" index cases were considered, and to 96 per cent when correction was made for noncompletion of the manifestation period for epilepsy.

	Both Twins Epileptic	One Twin Epileptic
Identical	20 (66.6%)	10
Fraternal	4 (3.1%)	126

The contrast between identical and fraternal twins is very striking and indicates that heredity has a great deal to do with the most frequent forms of epilepsy. This is borne out also by the increased incidence of seizure cases among the relatives of the index cases, as demonstrated by Conrad and shown in Table XXI.

Lennox (1951), with E. L. and F. A. Gibbs, in various papers has studied the concordance of electroencephalograms in one-egg and two-egg twins of whom one twin, at least, had seizures. This work is the basis for the concept that in the genetic cases the heredity is for a basic dysrhythmia, which may or may not be attended by seizures. It is interesting that in twin pairs without prior brain damage both cotwins were epileptic in 84 per cent of the one-egg and 10 per cent of the two-egg twins. In pairs *with* brain damage, the corresponding incidences were 17 and 8 per cent. Similar concordances were found for the electroencephalographic patterns.

In attempting to get the family history of an index case, every student of convulsive seizures has encountered either an ignorance of the family history or an understandable unwillingness to disclose information about affected relatives. It is quite probable that all of the old studies on seizures were deficient in af-

TABLE XXI   The Increased Incidence of Convulsive Seizures in the Relatives of Conrad's Index Cases

	Incidence per 100
General population	0.3
Nephews and nieces	1.2
Children	6.3
Siblings	4.0
The other fraternal twin	3.1
The other identical twin	66.6

fected individuals because of the secrecy surrounding seizures. The study of Kimball and Hersh (1955) surmounted this difficulty because their index cases attended the White Special School of Detroit. At this public school for children with seizures there was a marked change in the attitude of the parents as soon as this complex disease was considered a school problem and the school was ready to accept the child, care for him when sick, give him a good lunch and provide adequate educational and transportation facilities. There the parents appeared anxious to bring out all the facts about the child's disease and to give the family history in detail, if it were known. They obtained 520 sibships for which the clinical findings and family history are regarded as accurate and reasonably complete. There is no way of knowing what bias was introduced by rejecting the many incomplete histories still present even in this favorable setting. Neither can one estimate the bias introduced by affected persons with mild cases who never attended the school. Nonetheless, the group is probably representative of the kinds of families that could be expected to appear for counseling.

If we leave out the index case (which Kimball and Hersh failed to remove), their data show 105 of the 776 siblings of the index patient had seizures (13.5 per cent) when one parent also had seizures. Where neither parent had seizures, 52 out of 550 siblings of the index patient were affected. This is 9.5 per cent and is close enough to 13.5 per cent to indicate dominance with low penetrance rather than recessive inheritance also with incomplete penetrance. It is interesting that for the entire 520 sibships there were 302 affected parents, or 57.6 per cent of the expected 520 parents for a dominant gene with full penetrance. Unfortunately, no correction for age of onset was made, so that the figures for the siblings, in the 520 pedigrees included, are too low.

One of the most unfortunate aspects of a broadside approach to such a complex set of entities as convulsive seizures is that the component diseases represent more than one genetic entity; therefore, no single hypothesis fits all the families. Future genetic refinements depend upon diagnostic advances that allow a separation of different types of seizures, with the possibility of a separate genetic study for each variety. Such diagnostic discrimination in modern genetic analysis appears in a paper on the genetics of convulsive disorders by Metrakos and Metrakos (1961). They confined themselves to seizures designated "centrencephalic" as defined in their paper. They started with 211 probands with a history of recurrent seizures, no obvious neuropathology other than the seizures and a centrencephalic electroencephalogram. They selected 112 control persons with normal or borderline electroencephalograms.

The Metrakoses studied some 11,000 relatives of the patients and the controls and found that 13.5 per cent of the parents of the patients and 12.7 per cent of the siblings had a history of convulsions. These were statistically highly significantly different from the 1.3 per cent and 4.7 per cent of the control parents and siblings.

Their probands were ascertained primarily on the basis of a highly specific type of epileptiform electroencephalogram. Consequently, electroencephalographic studies of the parents and siblings would be most instructive. However, among 195 parents of centrencephalic and 85 parents of control probands, there were about 14 per cent cerebral dysrhythmias in both groups. But it is of importance that 15 of the 195 parents of the centrencephalic group had this specific type of electroencephalogram, and only 2 of the 84 parents of the controls had it.

The picture for the siblings is strikingly different. When only centrencephalic electroencephalograms are considered, there were 36.8 per cent abnormal siblings of the patients and 8.7 per cent dysrhythmias in the siblings of the controls. Incidentally, the dysrhythmias in the control group seemed to appear in familial

congregations. The reason that the frequency of the centrencephalic dysryhthmia is so scarce in the parents relates to the
tendency of this pattern to disappear in the late teens; it is rare
in adults.

It seems quite clear that the centrencephalic type of electroencephalogram behaves as a good dominant in 4 to 16 year old
children but disappears as the person matures. The crucial question is that of the relation between the centrencephalic electroencephalogram and the history of clinical seizures. The authors
promised to provide the answer to this question in a subsequent
paper. However, it will probably resemble the suggestion put
forward in the first edition of this book, namely, that a head
injury or accident of some kind triggers the clinical symptoms
and that the same injury would have no effect if the dysrhythmia
were not present. On the other hand, it is possible that no environmental stimulus is necessary and that other genes present
are responsible for the symptoms in persons with dysrhythmia.
Their answer will be of the greatest significance if it permits an
evaluation of these alternatives.

As a result of newer instrumentation for the study of the
brain waves, we are probaby on the verge of many important
discoveries concerning convulsive seizures. The science of elec-
troencephalography is becoming more exact and useful as time
goes on. There is a correlation between abnormal electroen-
cephalographs and convulsive seizures. Furthermore, the test is
probably of value in detecting a predisposition to seizures in
apparently normal people.

During the Middle Ages in Scotland, any man with falling
sickness was "instantly" castrated; an epileptic woman and her
brood were buried alive. This was a rather rugged eugenics program. Today a few of our states forbid marriage of the epileptic.
However, these laws are generally ignored. A much more serious
situation for the epileptic is social pressure, which ranges from

careless ridicule to widespread discrimination against him in employment. The answers to the problems of the epileptic are individual and not general. Certainly one should *not* encourage the epileptic to marry, as he must expect some amount of social pressure against himself and his potential family. Persons with epilepsy frequently ask if it would be wise for them to have children. The clinical data show that there is a chance of seizures of from 1 to 20 to 1 in 40 for each child. The chance is only 1 in 70 that the seizures will become chronic. As this is a moderate risk, the severity of the convulsive disorder is often a more important factor than the possibility of having affected children. In spite of new medications, there are many for whom seizures are still a tremendous problem. In such cases, it is not sensible to jeopardize the future of children yet unborn, because, normal or affected, they will be born into a family that can be expected to be visited by recurring misfortune.

It is important to summarize, as best we can, the data useful for genetic counseling. Some cases of seizures may well be the direct result of accidents and have no genetic predisposition. We don't know the proportion of seizure cases of this type, and it is always risky to assume that no genetic predisposition is present. If parents have produced a child with seizures, there is an average expectation of about 10 per cent that each subsequent child will be affected also. Each family has an expectation that may be quite different from 10 per cent, and no one can compute these individual family probabilities. However, it is helpful to parents to learn about the average experience of others and particularly to learn that they always have some chance of having some normal children. There are still no satisfactory data on the likelihood that a person with seizures, selected at random, will produce a child with seizures, and we do not know the percentage of children with seizures expected from a parent with dysrhythmia but no seizures. Nor do we know the percentage of affected children expected when both parents have dysrhythmia but no seizures. We can reassure these parents-to-be that the chances of each child having seizures are small, presumably from 1 in 20 to 1 in 40. The electroencephographer and geneticist still have much work to do in this field.

ILLUSTRATIVE EXAMPLES

1.   *Request.*
A theology student reported that his brother developed seizures during service in the navy but that there was no known trauma or other correlated external cause. The student wanted to know what was the likelihood that his potential children would have seizures.

Reply.
It was suggested that the student and his wife both obtain electroencephalogram records. This was done, the student's tracing was read, and the impression was that he had petit mal type seizures, though in actuality he has never yet had a seizure. His wife's record was normal. It would seem that the student is genetically epileptic, though without phenotypic manifestations of the disease. The couple was advised that each of their possible future children would have about 1 chance in 40 of having seizures.

Follow-up.
Apparently the couple considered 1 chance in 40 to be good odds. Five years after the counseling they had produced four children, none affected so far.

2.   *Request.*
When I was 13 years old, I had my first seizure. It was of the grand mal idiopathic type, and I have had at least one every two years since then. I take one and one-half grains of phenobarbital every night. My sister had her first seizure when she was about the same age. My mother and her mother had migraine headaches in conjunction with their menses. My migraine headaches never reached the intensity that my mother's did.

My seizures were very frequent between 1934 and 1937, and I was at the state hospital for epileptics during 1935–36 and contracted tuberculosis there. I was then in various hospitals for the next three years. Dr. R., who administered my pneumothorax, said that as far as the T.B. was concerned, I could have children. Dr. G. said that epilepsy was not thought to be as great a hereditary factor as it once was. Dr. G. K. thought it would be just easier to adopt a child(ren). Dr. L. K. fitted me for a diaphragm, and he said: Epilepsy is *not* transmittible, but in view of your tubercular history I think it is wise that you have a diaphragm." Dr. H. B. said that inasmuch as I had shown the fortitude to overcome both the tuberculosis and the epilepsy, he didn't see any reason why I shouldn't have children. On these opinions we decided that the balance was in our favor and so had a baby. He appears to be normal in every respect, and will be one and one-half years old in September.

However, we read recently in *Hygeia* that the chances of an epileptic parent producing epileptic offspring were 1 in 10. This seems to us to be a narrow margin to operate on, and before considering having any more children we would like to know what your opinion is as to the production of epileptic offspring.

Reply.

An interesting feature of your family has been the presence of migraine. We know that epileptics have an increased number of relatives with migraine. The two are related in some as yet obscure manner. The fact that both are present indicates strongly the hereditary features of these diseases in your family.

Studies have shown that 2 to 10 per cent of the children of an epileptic will develop the disease, with the larger risk relating to parents who have shown severe epilepsy, often with mental retardation.

Because of the frequently hereditary nature of epilepsy, some people think that epileptics should not have children. In your case, the problem is further complicated by your history of tuberculosis. There is no guarantee that, with more children and housework, the disease will not reappear. Should that occur, it would be difficult to rear either your own or adopted children. Being an epileptic yourself, you are familiar with the pitfalls and frustrations that such a disease provides for both the patient and her family. Having had a child, your husband and you know that you have what it takes to produce one. Perhaps you could best enjoy the situation as it is now, without tempting fate with further children, who might be affected with one or the other of the diseases that kept you in the hospital almost half of your adult life.

3. *Request.*

We [a county welfare department] are writing to you at this time to ask information on the hereditary nature of epilepsy. Our division has been asked to help in locating the mother of an 18 year old girl who was placed for adoption shortly after birth. The adoptive parents are reluctant to have her find her mother. However, the girl says that she will go on her own to find her. The adoptive parents and the girl know the mother's name, which they got from the adoption papers, as well as her address. We have located the true mother, and in addition to other negative features of her home, we find that she is subject to fits of epilepsy, although they did not develop until she was 30 years old.

There can be no doubt that the girl can find her mother. We do not feel that it would be wise for this girl to call upon her mother unannounced or without preparation in regard to the epilepsy. We have made no move to unite the girl with her mother and will not do so until she makes further efforts of her own. However, we wish to have as complete an evaluation of the situation as possible in advance.

Reply.
        I can understand the reluctance of the adoptive parents to have the girl develop an association with her own mother. No doubt the adoptive parents have expended a lot of their resources on the girl and would hate to see her drop in social level. Your concern that the girl will learn about the epilepsy and then worry about the possibility of having it herself is also justifiable.

Fortunately, the types of epilepsy that develop *after* about age 30 seem to have little, if any, tendency to run in families. As the girl has not had any seizures, the chance of her ever having the disease is very small, probably less than 1 per cent. As the chance is so small, it would seem best if the girl did not find her own mother and were not told about the epilepsy. How she can be prevented from doing so is another question.

The following example is of a situation that the uninformed public would consider decidedly dysgenic. There are certainly problems here for the future, the question being whether they will be serious problems or merely the usual exasperations everyone is subjected to. It is the problem of marriage and reproduction by persons who both have a handicap.

Request.
        A young lady and her fiancé came in. She has both grand mal and petit mal seizures, but they are under fair medical control and she functions well, as an office receptionist. Now and then she has a seizure under embarrassing conditions. The fiancé has cerebral palsy that affects his gait but with no speech or mental involvement. He admits to wide mood swings, also present in his father. He is in the

"manic" stage most of the time, which has been to his advantage. The couple stated their intention to marry, but they had fixed on the idea that their children would have a 40 per cent chance of having seizures. They were apprehensive whether they should have any children.

Reply.

There was no pedigree of seizures, and the chance of having their first child affected with seizures is certainly less than 40 per cent. Married people should have children unless there are contra-indications of an important nature. They realized that they were handicapped to some extent and should therefore limit their family size.

Follow-up.

The couple married but have not had any children as yet. However, they seem most confident that they will have some. The wife still has her job and has the makings of a career woman. This will probably help keep the family at a modest size.

Chapter 25

THE SCHIZOPHRENIAS

Mental disorders represent the last line of resistance to mendelian genetics. Psychiatrists have little choice but to accept the clear-cut dominant mendelian pedigrees for neurologic diseases such as Marie's cerebellar ataxia and Huntington's chorea, but many are emotionally unprepared to accept the idea that heredity has anything to do with psychoses. This is strange indeed, because Freud was well aware of the constitutional or genetic basis for mental illnesses. Psychiatrists do not usually accept patients for psychoanalysis where the disorders appear to be "biologic," although recent advances in therapy have been through the physiologic control of behavior by tranquilizers and other physical treatments.

The reason that geneticists have failed to present clear-cut mendelian pedigrees for the schizophrenias is that, like many physical ailments, they are too frequent to have a simple genetic basis. The schizophrenias are the most common of the psychoses. It is generally accepted that from 1 to 5 per cent of the population is affected with schizophrenia at some time. Scientific understanding is hampered by the almost overwhelming problems involved in diagnosis, but we cannot wait for the psychiatrists to solve these problems before genetic studies are commenced. Schizophrenia is an urgent problem; it is a severe drain on the resources of the whole world.

Some psychiatrists reject the concept of a genetic basis for psychoses because they have the false idea that genetic diseases cannot be cured. If the patients believed in heredity, which they usually do, it might retard their therapy. Thus, genetics is a threat to psychiatrists. However, turning one's face against the facts will not lead to progress, and it will be recalled from previous chapters that the genotype can often be overruled when we learn how to do it. It is still difficult to know where to start with prevention at a nonmedical level or whether this is a promising field of endeavor. The famous studies of Hollingshead and Redlich (1958) indicate that the lowest social class has the highest incidence of schizophrenia. It is no surprise that conditions in the bottom stratum of New Haven society are conducive to schizophrenia. The critical question seems to be why the differences between the frequencies of schizophrenia in the five social classes were not much greater than observed!

Let us see if any conclusions can be derived as to possible genetic backgrounds for any of the schizophrenias.

It is well to look to the material from twins first to ascertain the strength of heredity in the expression of schizophrenia. We are indebted to Kallmann (1946 and 1953) for the largest twin study of this or any other disease. These publications include an analysis of 691 schizophrenic twin index families. The 1946 publication contains the data that are used here, as they are most conveniently arranged in that paper. The comparison of the two kinds of twins and their agreement or disagreement

TABLE XXII   The   Expression   of Schizophrenia in Twins

	Both Twins with Schizophrenia	One Twin with Schizophrenia
Identical	120 (69%)	54
Fraternal	53 (10%)	464

in both or only one having schizophrenia is shown in Table XXII.

The differences in concordance and discordance of the two types of twins are statistically highly significant. The data agree extremely well with those of other investigators collected by Stern (1960), which showed 68 per cent agreement for identical twins and 11 per cent agreement for fraternals.

The age of onset of schizophrenia varies over several years, so age corrections should be made, as was done by Kallmann. After this procedure, the expected concordance is raised to 86 per cent for the one-egg twins and to 15 per cent for the two-egg twins. The high concordance between the genetically identical twins is evidence of a strong hereditary background for schizophrenia. Further support for this statement comes from a comparison of the other close relatives of schizophrenic twins, as shown in Table XXIII.

It is significant that the incidence of schizophrenia in the other two-egg twin (15 per cent) is practically the same as in the other single-birth siblings (14 per cent). Apparently the similar family environment of the two-egg twins is not sufficiently different from that of ordinary brothers and sisters to cause any

TABLE XXIII   The Expression of Schizophrenia in Relatives of the Twin Index Cases

Relationship	Corrected Morbidity Rate
Spouse	2%
Stepsiblings	2%
Half siblings	7%
Parents	9%
Full siblings	14%
Two-egg twin	15%
One-egg twin	86%

change in the incidence of schizophrenia. The twin studies indicate that the basic environmental factors involved are *internal* to the individual and are concerned fundamentally with metabolic and physiologic changes; see Kallmann (1948).

A bright idea of Rosenthal (1959) produced most interesting results. He considered only monozygous twins and reasoned that there should be a history of schizophrenic illness more frequently in the families of concordant than of discordant identical twins. Thus, if there is a subgroup of schizophrenia that has little hereditary basis, it should be found among the discordant identical twins more often than among the concordant twins. Rosenthal then examined the family history data for Slater's 37 monozygotic twin pairs and found the following sharp dichotomy of the data:

	Family History Positive for Schizophrenic Illness	Family History Negative for Schizophrenic Illness
Concordant pairs	13	9
Discordant pairs	1	12

The association between discordance of the identical twins and a lack of affected relatives is striking. It was found also that the type of illness in the discordant pairs was a relatively late onset and of benign outcome compared with the concordant pairs. All pairs were identical twins. For other interesting analyses of other workers' data, see Rosenthal (1961).

The problem of whether the heredity of schizophrenia is that of a single recessive, a single dominant or some more complicated genetic mechanism is not so easy to resolve. Kallmann's choice was that of a recessive, but it would seem technically more nearly correct to interpret his data as showing the inheritance of an abnormal gene with incomplete dominance. The reason for this suggested change in terminology stems from the large group of "schizoidias," which have been omitted from the tables in this chapter but which must be accounted for in some way. Kallmann stated: "The schizoid types must be regarded as the heterozygotic carriers of the schizophrenic taint." If this is true, with the heterozygote phenotypically detectable, we have incomplete dominance by definition. Kallmann actually meant, it seems, that the schizophrenics are homozygous for the abnormal gene in contrast to the schizoids, who are assumed to be heterozygous. We should call the abnormal gene an incomplete dominant, rather than a recessive, if the schizoids are phenotypically distinguishable from the "normal" members of the population; this seems to be the case.

The conclusion follows that the abnormal gene is an incomplete dominant, resulting in a schizoid person when present in a single dose and the schizophrenic patient when present in the double dose.

In all probability this last conclusion is an over-simplification. It is likely that the strength of the dominance varies from family pedigree to family pedigree, thus giving some histories that look like dominant inheritance with incomplete penetrance and others that appear to be recessive. In human genetics we have to keep clearly in mind the common phenomenon that genes at different loci on the same or on unrelated chromosomes may have indistinguishable phenotypic expressions.

The difficulties of genetic classification for schizophrenia are very similar to those for diabetes and for the same reasons. In both cases the abnormal gene is very frequent in the population, and expression of the character may not come until late in life; in some cases it will never be detected clinically. It is not particularly important for counseling whether these genes behave as recessives or incomplete dominants because they are common in the population and the empiric risk figures dictate what the statistical expectations are to be. But for rare traits it is of importance to know whether the heredity is that of a good dominant or a recessive because such knowledge has prognostic value.

It is probably impossible, genetically speaking, to make any absolute distinction between mental and physical diseases. Both mental and physical diseases have complicated genetics if they are common and simple mendelian heredity if they are rare. Of course, there are exceptions to this generalization relating the rare disease to a clear-cut type of heredity. However, schizophrenia would be expected to show an elusive type of heredity, or at least a considerable influence of the environment upon its expression, because it is so prevalent.

The reader should not forget that the intellectual advantage that we have over the ameba is perpetuated by our heredity. This heredity is present in the cells of the brain, and the basic potentialities for mental health or disease reside in those cells and are determined by their heredity. Heredity, as a factor in mental disease, must therefore be accepted and evaluated. For most persons, the precise mechanism of the heredity involved is of secondary importance. The crux of the argument is whether schizophrenia has an heredity of some sort or whether it is acquired, as is a knowedge of a foreign language.

It should not be thought that the evidence for heredity comes only from Kallmann. A large and most careful study of the whole population of the three most northeastern parishes of Sweden has been published by Böök (1953). This study did not employ the twin method, but it comes out with results comparable to those of Kallmann for the appropriate comparisons. For Böök's population the morbid risk for parents of schizophrenic propositi was 12.0±2.7 per cent, which is close enough to Kallmann's 9 per cent (Table XXIII) to be a satisfactory agreement. As can be seen in this table, the risk for full siblings of the schizophrenic patient is 14 per cent, while Böök found a somewhat lower figure of about 10 per cent. The deviations between the results of these two exhaustive studies seem to be random in nature.

The evidence from all the careful studies to date indicates very clearly that the closer the genetic relationship to the schizophrenic patient, the greater the chance of developing the disease. The most reasonable interpretation of this fact is that schizophrenia has a genetic basis and that the expression of the heredity is subject to the total environment encountered. Fortunately, the environment can be improved in some cases and the patient gets well. Furthermore, a proper understanding of the physiologic and psychologic environment may at some time allow us to prevent the disease from appearing in the first place.

At present our information on the appearance of schizophrenia among the offspring of schizophrenics is meager indeed. A follow-up study of the offspring of schizophrenic patients of a generation ago is badly needed. An estimate of the frequency of affected offspring when one parent has the disease is perhaps one-sixth and when both parents have it, one-half. The latter figure is based on a very few families and will therefore have a very large sampling error.

Once again it should be emphasized that the expectation for children of schizophrenics is very important and follow-up studies should be made. Such information would be invaluable for adoption agencies, which frequently have babies to place, one or both of whose parents were schizophrenic. Furthermore, the adoption agencies themselves should make follow-up studies of the adjustments of the children whom they have placed, one or both of whose true parents were schizophrenic. This not only would provide the information the agencies want but would permit an evaluation of the possible improvement resulting from the new environment compared with the children from affected parents who stayed with their true parents.

There are several interesting cases in the literature of schizophenic attacks in both members of identical twin pairs. The following illustrative example emphasizes again that identical twins seem to develop their difficulties at almost precisely the same time, which indicates that both reach almost simultaneously a physiologic threshold that permits development of the symptoms. The specific exciting stimulus may be quite different, as in the case below, and its precise nature is relatively unimportant. It should be remembered, however, that identical twins are *not* always concordant for schizophrenia. A careful study of the physiologic differences between the discordant twins may provide the clues needed for a medical cure and prevention of the disease.

ILLUSTRATIVE EXAMPLES

1.   These identical twins were highly intelligent students in high school. Their grades were identical in all except one course in which one got an A and the other a B. On the basis of this difference one was chosen to be the valedictorian and the other the salutatorian of the class. Both did commendable work at the University of Minnesota. One of the twins married a very presentable and considerate man and seemed happy with him. The other may have been somewhat upset by this event; at any rate she went to China to teach English. Apparently she was greatly disappointed at the failure of the Chinese government to provide facilities she had expected. She soon developed catatonia and had to be flown back to California, where she was placed in an institution for treatment.

Almost simultaneously the Minnesota sister developed an obsession that her father was not looking after her mother adequately. There seems to have been no particular real change in the family relations of the parents. She was further disturbed by the fact that her husband did not think it advisable to start a family under the cir-

cumstances. She entered the University Hospitals in a state of catatonia. The question referred to the Dight Institute was as follows.

Request.
 If the patient recovers, should the couple be advised to have
a child? What are the chances that it would develop schizophrenia?

Reply.
 The evidence for an hereditary background here is quite striking. The child could be expected to have about one chance in six of
developing schizophrenia.

A more important consideration is whether the patient's recovery can be expected to be permanent. The most careful study on
the prognosis for schizophrenia known to me is that of Stenberg
(1948). In it he shows that for women, 10 years after the first attack, 16 per cent have stably recovered, 12 per cent have instably
recovered and 72 per cent were permanently ill.

Considering the fact that the possible child has a reasonable
expectancy of developing the disease and that the prognosis for a
permanent cure for the mother is not bright, it would be folly to
encourage this couple to have children, at least until it is clear
whether the marriage is to be successful or not.

Follow-up.
 The advice was fully justified. The marriage fell apart very
soon and a divorce followed. Fortunately, there were no children.
The two sisters have had two subsequent episodes with simultaneous
hospitalization. Both are "well" at present and, because of their high
intelligence, have no difficulty in supporting themselves. Obviously,
it is better for them to remain single and childless.

Second Follow-up.
 The author had nothing to do with the situation, but he can
report that the sisters have not married and it is now unlikely that
either one will ever have any children. It is of great interest that one
of the sisters has had an episode lately that the psychiatrist states
was of the manic-depressive type rather than schizophrenic. She recovered, and the other twin had no difficulty that time. The same
psychiatrist has treated the twins for all episodes, except the one in
China, and insists that the last one, experienced by only one of the
twins, is most certainly different from any previous attack. This episode exposes the fundamental problem of diagnosis.

2.   A baby girl is in custody of a county welfare board. At the

present time the father is on parole from the state hospital. He is now 22 and became schizophrenic at age 18. The mother is schizophrenic and is in the state hospital. She has been mentally ill since 18 years of age but was committed only recently. Both parents of the child are alike in being young and schizophrenic. The grandmother feels that she has nothing to offer the child as she is very suspicious that the child will become mentally ill in due course also. Consequently, the county has assumed responsibility and wishes to know the prognosis for adoption.

Request.

We are interested in finding out whether this child is adoptable. Therefore, we would like you to give us some idea of the chances that this baby will develop mental illness.

Reply.

Research by Kallmann and others gives risk figures for determining the chances you request. When both parents are schizophrenic, each child has an even chance of developing the disease before the end of adult life. If one of identical twins develops schizophrenia, there is an 86 per cent chance that the other twin will become schizophrenic. Presumably all children from a schizophrenic pair of parents have the genes that allow the disease to become manifest if the environmental situation becomes favorable for development of the disease. Apparently the environment becomes favorable for the expression of the disease for half of those who qualify genetically, as does this baby. We do not consider her a good risk for adoption. It is quite unusual for us to consider a baby a poor adoptive risk, but schizophrenia seems to us to be one of the most serious of many possible diseases.

Request.

A most attractive and capable woman presented the following story. She has five children by her first husband. He is now schizophrenic and a patient in a state hospital. The three oldest children have had hospital treatment for personality and behavioral problems. The woman recently married a man who seems to be similar to her first husband. If things don't go just right, he is inclined to break up one of the living room chairs and burn it in the fireplace. His attitude toward the oldest daughter is unwholesome. The woman has had two miscarriages by the second husband and wonders whether she should attempt another pregnancy because of the possibility that the child might inherit the father's mental difficulties.

It is impossible to include here all of the details of the investigations that took place, but essentially it was important for the woman to see that heredity was not the primary problem so far as her second husband was concerned. One problem was to restore her relationship with the head of the family counseling section, who had advised her *not* to marry the second husband; another was to get the husband to accept psychiatric help.

Follow-up.

In spite of her numerous problems, this woman continues to function at a high level in the business world; she has had no further pregnancies.

Chapter 26

MANIC-DEPRESSIVE
PSYCHOSIS

There are various ways of investigating the influence of heredity in relation to a particular disease. The twin method has been considered already. The method of studying a genetic isolate is also of great value. Böök (1953) has done an especially fine job of working with neuropsychiatric diseases in such an isolated area, namely, the three most northeastern parishes in Sweden. The area is mainly forest and boglands and is some 50 miles north of the Arctic Circle. Communications were very poor until the 1920s, and there were still no railways within the area in 1953. The general mobility of the population, as measured by crude migration rates, had been rather low. The incidences of marriages between first cousins, among all marriages existing in 1947, was 2.2±0.4 per cent, a high rate, which one might expect in an isolated area. The area has a pronounced rural character and in 1949 had a population of 8,981 persons.

This isolate of 8,981 persons provided 364 individuals who were insane, mentally defective or epileptic. The affected persons belonged to 285 parent-sibship combinations and a total of 10,341 of their ancestors were investigated in the records. Of these, 240 sibships could be joined into one large pedigree complex that went back to 31 ancestral pairs living about 1700 to 1750. *Con-*

sequently, the large majority of affected individuals were genetically related.

The next remarkable point was that, when proper longevity corrections were made, the expectation for a person developing schizophrenia was practically 3 per cent, slightly higher than usual estimates for clear-cut cases of the disease. Practically all the cases were diagnosed by other physicians as well as by Böök. Böök had 120 cases of schizophrenia available for analysis of the symptomatology. In contrast to this strikingly high incidence of schizophrenia, only one person seemed to be suffering from manic-depressive psychosis and properly belonged to the study; one other apparently certain case was a migrant. Thus, at least as a major psychotic state, the manic-depressive type was practically nonexistent in the investigation area. This is in spite of the depressing climate of the region.

Let us now consider a second genetic rural isolate, the Hutterites of the northern United States and Canada. This group was composed of 8,542 persons, practically all descended from 101 married couples and their children who came to the United States between 1874 and 1877. The Hutterites and the North Swedish groups are samples of the same size; both are rural and short on formal education, and both marry within their genetic isolate. In both cases the groups have descended from a small number of somewhat related individuals. Under such circumstances, we might expect some genes to become established and spread to some extent in the genetic isolate while others will be lost from the group. This process of fixation or elimination of particular genes during the history of a closed group of persons is called genetic drift and should be detectable in these small groups.

While Böök found practically no manic-depressive psychosis in his North Swedish population, Eaton and Weil (1953) found 74 cases of manic depression and only 17 cases of schizophrenia in the Hutterite population, which was screened and diagnosed with great care. It is most interesting that Eaton, a sociologist, and Weil, a psychiatrist, started their study of the Hutterites on the assumption that there would be little mental illness in this group. "They live a simple, rural life, have a harmonious social order and provide every member with a high level of economic security from the womb to the tomb." However, instead of discovering the environmental road to mental health, they found the highest frequency of manic depression so far recorded for any population!

The study of Eaton and Weil showed that, while the Hutterite culture could not prevent the appearance of mental disorders, because of their genetic nature, it did provide a highly therapeutic atmosphere for their treatment. The onset of symptoms served as a signal for the entire community to demonstrate support and love for the patients. They received great encouragement and were considered to be ill rather than "crazy." In this rigidly stereotyped culture, the mental illnesses have about the same prognoses as they do in any other culture.

While both of these studies gave clear evidence of heredity, neither the North Swedish nor the Hutterite study provided much information about the type of heredity concerned with manic-depressive psychosis, although the Hutterite group might become a fertile source of high-quality data.

There is a fair sized literature on the heredity of manic-depressive psychosis that makes use of the traditional methods of twin study and pedigree analysis. Much of this information has been collected by Kallmann (1953). The influence of heredity is somewhat stronger for manic depression than it is for schizophrenia, as may be seen by comparing Tables XXIV and XXII. If the data for the fraternal twins are corrected for longevity, the expected rate of the psychosis in the cotwin rises from 19 per cent for schizophrenia to 26 per cent for manic depression.

Kallmann's data for manic-depressive psychosis, expressed in the same way as previously shown for schizophrenia in Table XXIII, are presented in Table XXV. We see that the frequency of the disease in spouses is very low, but in blood relatives it is higher than for schizophrenia. An important point is that the age

TABLE XXIV   The Expression of Manic-Depressive Psychosis in Twins (Uncorrected)

	Both Twins with the Psychosis	One Twin with the Psychosis
Identical	22 (96%)	1
Fraternal	10 (19%)	42

of onset of manic depression is later than for schizophrenia. The manic-depressive person has usually lived with his spouse longer than he did with his blood relatives. Transmission of the disease therefore seems to be more of the longitudinal type, expected on a genetic basis, than of the contemporary type shown by bacterial epidemics. Full siblings gave a corrected expectation of 23 per cent and parents 23 per cent, there being no biologic difference between these findings. This agreement among the fraternal twins, their sibs and parents indicates a dominant gene for the psychosis that expresses itself in about 50 per cent of

TABLE XXV   The Expression of Manic-Depressive Psychosis in Relatives of the Twin Index Cases

Relationship	Corrected Morbidity Rate
Spouse	<1%
Half siblings	17%
Parents	23%
Full siblings	23%
Two-egg twins	26%
One-egg twins	100%

those persons having the gene. Similar results have been obtained in Sweden by Stenstedt (1952).

Once again we have no adequate follow-up study of the children of manic-depressive patients, the reason being that it is necessary to wait one generation after the patient is diagnosed before the offspring reach the age of onset and can be expected to show symptoms. However, if the inheritance is that of a single dominant gene with incomplete penetrance, we would expect between 20 and 30 per cent of the offspring of the patient to develop the disease when they reach the age of onset for it. Stenstedt (1952) thinks that the risk of manic-depressive psychosis for the siblings, parents and children of most patients is about 15 per cent.

Merrell (1951) analyzed the data in the literature and was able to eliminate all the theories of heredity involving only one gene locus, except that of an autosomal dominant with incomplete penetrance. Dr. Merrell also made a preliminary study of records of manic-depressive families of a generation ago. Between 1912 and 1918 the pedigrees of manic-depressive patients at the Warren State Hospital, Warren, Pennsylvania, were collected by Mrs. A. D. Finlayson for the Eugenics Records Office, Cold Spring Harbor, New York. The records now belong to the Dight Institute for Human Genetics. Dr. Merrell selected records for patients only when there was little doubt about the diagnosis. It is remarkable that for the many relatives who were institutionalized in other hospitals and in other states, the diagnosis was almost always also manic depression and not the more common schizophrenia.

Dr. Merrell found higher percentages of manic-depressive psychosis among the parents and siblings of the patients than other workers have. This is probably due to the fact that most of these persons had completed their lives by the time of his follow-up study and thus most cases had an opportunity to come to expression; furthermore, his selection of only those patients who had obviously been manic-depressives may have been also an indirect selection for those families in which the gene was highly penetrant.

It is interesting that Dr. Merrell was able to demonstrate a clear-cut relation of suicide to manic-depressive psychosis in the small population he studied. Among some 1,600 blood relatives of the manic-depressive patients, there were 32 cases of suicide, that is, 2 per cent. Among 1,000 in-laws of the patients, there were only 2 cases of suicide, or 0.2 per cent, about normal expectation. Thus, the blood relatives of the patients showed 10 times the normal suicide rate. Similar results have been obtained by other investigators (see Stenstedt, 1952).

In summary, the available evidence shows that the hereditary basis for manic-depressive psychosis is stronger than that for schizophrenia. This would be expected, as manic depression is not nearly as common as schizophrenia. The heredity for manic-depressive psychosis is apparently due to a dominant gene with incomplete penetrance. With manic depression the dominant gene expresses itself more frequently and severely than does the incomplete dominant for schizophrenia. This would suggest that environmental variables are more important in the onset of schizophrenia than of manic-depressive psychosis. The present oversimplified concepts of the genetics of mental disorders are the most intellectually economical ones. They are also the most practical ones for counseling in medical genetics. However, our present knowledge indicates future subdivisions of diagnosis into a perhaps fairly large number of distinct diseases, each with a separate genetic basis. At present we have only empiric risk figures, which give average expectations for the transmission of mental illness from one generation to the next. It should not be forgotten that this transmission will occur regardless of the relative strengths of heredity and environment. Unfortunately, we still have no way of predicting which individuals will be the victims, although such tests as the Minnesota Multiphasic Personality Inventory can give some hints even in children.

ILLUSTRATIVE EXAMPLE

Practically all the clients that have come to us for counseling in regard to manic-depressive psychosis have presented pedigrees loaded with suicides and manic-depressive psychosis. In these families the pattern of transmission suggests dominant inheritance almost as much as pedigrees for Huntington's chorea. These families have behaved as if a dominant gene with fairly high penetrance were present. The sample coming to a genetic counseling center is certainly biased toward high heritability, so *minimum* risk figures are not very realistic for them. Thus, a range from minimum to maximum risks should be given, with the explanation that there is no way of knowing just where the family fits into the range as far as future generations are concerned.

Chapter 27

GENETIC EFFECTS OF
RADIATIONS

It has been known for a long time that radiations with wave lengths of about 10^{-6} cm. or under cause mutations in laboratory organisms. H. J. Muller's famous discovery of the fact that an environmental agent such as x-rays can alter the gene won him a Nobel prize. Since Muller's publication in 1927, a vast amount of work has been done with irradiations as a source of genetic mutations, and there can be no doubt that there is a direct relationship between the amount of energy put into the chromosome and the number of genetic mutations obtained. Theoretically, no dosage is too small to produce a single mutation in a single cell of the body. Actually, we are continuously subjected to irradiation from natural sources such as cosmic rays.

No controlled experiments on the production of mutations in man have been carried out, for the simple reason that scientists do not indulge in experiments that are expected to be harmful to human beings. In warfare the goal is to be as harmful to as many of the enemy soldiers as possible and at once. If one must die as a war casualty, it would be preferable (to me) to die in an atomic bomb explosion rather than on the point of a spear; this philosophy helped justify the use of the atomic bombs on Hiroshima and Nagasaki, which did end the war with Japan promptly. Undoubtedly the bombs saved many Japanese and American lives that otherwise would have been lost had the war continued with the slow recapture of territory by conventional methods. Thus, in fact, if President Truman had prohibited the use of the two atomic bombs in Japan, he would have been responsible for many more deaths than actually occurred. The two bombs demonstrated conclusively that any possible future world wars will be short because of the catastrophic effects of even a few of the modern bombs. Consequently, I am optimistic that atomic bombs will not be used again. It should be remembered that both sides refrained from using gruesome poisonous gases in World War II.

Considerable scientific information was gleaned from the havoc wrought by the atomic bombings. A study was made of the children conceived by persons who had been irradiated during the bombing. Neel and Schull (1956) and their collaborators published their findings on the possible genetic damage done to these children. It was apparent to the group from the beginning that the demonstrable genetic effects of the irradiation at Hiroshima and Nagasaki would probably be so small as to be of doubtful statistical significance. This was the case. A gross chromosome change would result in the immediate elimination of the cell in many cases, whereas recessive gene mutations might not become homozygous, and thus visible, for hundreds of years. Consequently, no large increase in damage to each future generation will occur.

Does this mean that irradiations are not harmful? Of course not; it means that the only possible "design of experiment" could not provide the type of information that would be illuminating. We already have such a large load of old harmful mutations on hand that a small addition of new ones is undetectable. Should there be an all-out atomic war in the future, the population might be reduced to very small numbers. However, the genetic heritage for the future would be in much better condition than the cultural heritage. The reasons why surviving mankind will not become extinct as a consequence of increased genetic mutations are presented in a most interesting and readable little book by Wallace and Dobzhansky (1959). The argument is that, while a whole-body dose of 500 to 1,000 roentgens would cause death, it is not a high enough dose to destroy all of the reproductive cells. Thus, the survivors will have received less than this dose, and a sufficient number of their eggs or sperms will be viable to produce a new generation.

However, irradiations certainly do damage cells, and it is possible to get an approximate idea of the extent of damage by irradiating, and then observing, the chromosomes of human cells growing in tissue culture. Bender and Wolff (1961) showed that the dose required to break at least one chromosome in two in each cell of human epithelioid cells *in vitro* was only about 190 roentgens. Another approach is to look at the chromosomes of the white blood cells drawn from a person before x-ray therapy, as the control, and then at the chromosomes in samples drawn from the same person at various times after the therapy. This was done by Tough, Buckton, Baikie and Court-Brown (1960). In a patient treated with 250 rads for ankylosing spondylitis there were chromosome abnormalities in 9 to 10 per cent of the cells as late as the fifth day after exposure. This dose would not be enough to sterilize the person, but it would be sufficient to cause one or more mutations, which could be expected to result in damage or death for some of this person's descendants.

One must accept the fact that the medical use of radiation is dangerous and undoubtedly results in deleterious mutations and deaths in subsequent generations. This does *not* mean that the medical use of x-rays should be discouraged. It means, however, that careless use of x-rays is absolutely inexcusable. There is a great deal of irresponsible and careless use of x-rays by a few physicians; this should be remedied. Inspections show that poor maintenance of private office machines is frequent among physicians but less frequent among dentists.

One practice that makes the geneticist's hair stand on end is treatment of female sterility by irradiation of the ovaries. Kaplan (1958) reported that he treated 700 cases of female sterility by irradiation and 308 women had 540 living children; of whom 35 had grown up and produced in turn 43 children, with no defects noted. Kaplan thought that his experience showed how safe his technique was. However, there is no way of demonstrating statistically how many recessive mutations he may have produced. As with the havoc at Hiroshima, we can expect the new recessives to meet similar ones gradually and be expressed for the first time hundreds of years from now. Even though these deaths may not occur until the distant future, the moral problem remains. Each case of harm or death due to careless irradiation, in our time or in the distant future, places a burden on our conscience.

In concluding, it may be well to try to get some perspective on the magnitude of the radiation problem. Even though we cannot see, smell, taste or feel radiations, they are a part of our lives. It is estimated that during the 30 years of the average person's reproductive capacity he receives the equivalent of 5 roentgens in background natural radiations. According to present calculations, the average person receives 3 roentgens from medical radiations. This is an "unfair" figure: hardly anyone receives exactly 3 roentgens. Most people receive no medical x-rays at all, while a few might have as much as 3,500 roentgens directed toward, say, a cervical cancer. The dose from bomb-testing fallout is less than 10 per cent of the medical "average" up to the present, that is, less than a calculated 0.3 roentgens for a 30 year reproductive life. As various scientists have pointed out, elevated body temperature due to overly warm clothing has undoubtedly caused more deleterious mutations up to now than has fallout radiation. It should not be forgotten that there are many mutagenic agents, such as heat and some chemicals, in addition to radiation.

The National Research Council Committee has estimated that 30 to 80 roentgens constitutes a "doubling dose"; that is, this dose would double the spontaneous mutation rate from all causes over what it had been in the past. The committee recommended a "maximum permissible dose" of 10 roentgens to the gonads during the period from conception to age 30. If 50 roentgens is the average doubling dose, a population receiving an average of 10 roentgens would show a 20 per cent increase in genetic damage. This represents an increase in abnormalities in children attributable to genetic mutations (old) of 2 per cent to 2.4 per cent (old and new). This is a heavy burden to carry each generation. No pains should be spared to keep our dose of radiation at the very lowest possible level. This is one area in which we should strive for the minimum and shun the maximum permissible dose. No dose, down to a single quantum of energy, can be guaranteed harmless. Rigid safety precautions are the only answer to our dilemma of increasing the profitable use of radiant energy while cutting the genetic cost of additional deleterious mutations.

ILLUSTRATIVE EXAMPLES

1.   *Request.*

A couple brought in their first child, who had hypospadias. The husband thought that it was his "fault" and that it resulted from extensive fluoroscopy, which he had experienced during the war. They were concerned with the possibility of a recurrence in subsequent children.

Reply.

It was explained that there was no way of being certain whether the anomaly was due to a mutation resulting from the paternal radiation or whether both parents might be carriers of a gene for hypospadias. The literature suggests autosomal recessive heredity with poor penetrance of less than 10 per cent as a genetic basis for the trait. In either case, there is no "fault" to be attributed to either parent. Fortunately, the chance of a repetition of the trait would be less than 10 per cent for either explanation. There was no reason why the couple should not go ahead with their family plans.

Follow-up.

The mother was contacted five years later and had to be reminded of her visit to the Dight Institute. Her son had had corrective surgery in the meantime and, except for a recent first attack of asthma, was in good health. She had had two normal boys since the visit, and it was clear that no one was worrying about a repetition of hypospadias.

2.   *Request.*

An obstetrician had the following problem: his patient became pregnant unexpectedly and wanted an abortion on the grounds of genetic damage to the child. Her husband had received radiation therapy for a seminoma of the testis. This fact was properly verified by the radiologist, who was also concerned about the situation.

Reply.

It was explained that the chance of genetic damage was not large, even for future generations, but it does exist. However, the treatment for the husband was absolutely necessary, and the radiologist had not been careless. The couple was persuaded that the chances of a defective child were so small that an abortion would not be justified. The baby had not been born at the time of writing. The follow-up will be interesting, particularly if the child should be abnormal for any reason whatever.

Chapter 28

THE ENVIRONMENT

The strongest genotype ever conceived could not develop in a vacuum. Thus, the study of genetics must always attempt to evaluate environmental variables, which can so easily confuse the genetic interpretation. The greatest single obstacle to success in animal or plant breeding is mistaking environmental variations for genetic improvements. If the "improved" animal is merely the result of a chance environmental fluctuation, the gain will not be transmitted to the offspring. One can never really distinguish between heredity and environment; the most that can be done is to demonstrate gene differences in a population, usually by showing their mendelian behavior in a group of pedigrees.

My duty as a geneticist is to attempt to demonstrate the genetic mechanisms involved for each human difference of interest. Genetic mechanisms must be present because we are the products of our heredity and our environment and, according to Muller, we are the genes' way of making more genes. However, the geneticist is intensely interested in the environmental factors that confuse the genetic picture and is delighted when an environmental factor can be pinned down. The sickle cell gene–malarial parasite story is one of the most brilliant research triumphs in science. The original mystery was why the gene for sickle cell anemia was practically nonexistent in, say, Sweden, but present in about 40 per cent of the members of some African

218

tribes. Allison (1955) showed that the sickle cell gene in one dose provides some protection against malaria so that where the malarial parasites abound the gene for sickle cell anemia will spread, even though it is lethal in the double dose, or homozygous condition. The parasite is an environmental agent, of course, and the local populations gradually evolve a genetic protection against it. In the United States, where malaria has been eliminated, the gene for sickle cell anemia is gradually being eliminated from the American Negro population, as it no longer has a protective function.

Perhaps the most celebrated effect of an environmental agent directly affecting the unborn is that produced by the rubella virus. This German measles virus is capable of crossing the placenta from mother to child, and the prenatal infection, if it occurs early enough, may result in deafness and other damage to the child. Similarly, maternal infection with the rare protozoan parasite *Toxoplasma* can cause serious congenital defects in the fetus, and the same has been suspected for Asian influenza.

I think it is fair to state that while much has been said about the great importance of prenatal infections, few well-designed experiments have been initiated. The rubella excitement is a case in point.

Although the relationship of congenital anomalies in the newborn to maternal rubella was established by Gregg (1941), there was no way of knowing what percentage of mothers had rubella during the first trimester of pregnancy and then produced a *normal* child. Other retrospective studies gave extremely high estimates, of 50 per cent or more, for abnormalities if the mother had rubella during the first trimester. These reports instilled such terror that many physicians were prepared to grant therapeutic abortions with little question.

The proper design of experiment is not a retrospective

study but rather a follow-up or prospective study. An epidemic of rubella began in 1955 in Montreal. A committee of the Montreal Obstetrical and Gynaecological Society was appointed to follow the women who had rubella during pregnancy. It observed 47 cases of rubella during pregnancy, reported by Oxorn (1959). Of the 47 women, 9 had rubella during the second or third trimester and all had healthy children. In 38 cases the rubella was contracted during the first trimester. Of these, 7 ended in abortion, 3 spontaneous, 2 induced and 2 missed. Thus, 31 women who had rubella in the first trimester carried the fetus to term. Of these, 25 had normal children; 6 babies (19 per cent) were born with congenital defects. The defect in 1, at least, of the 6 would seem to be unrelated to the rubella. Of the 6 abnormal children, 3 died and only 1 survivor had congenital cataracts; none was deaf. It is odd that only 1 mother among the 47 contracted rubella during her third trimester.

Other prospective studies, such as those of Greenberg, Pellitteri and Barton (1957) and of Lundström (1962), agree that malformations occur after rubella infection in the first trimester of pregnancy in from 9 to 12 per cent of the cases. Control women who did not acquire rubella have about 2 per cent malformations in their newborn progeny.

It is clear now that the woman who has been exposed to rubella during her first trimester of pregnancy has less than half the likelihood of an abnormal child than parents have who have proved themselves to be carriers of a recessive for Hurler's syndrome, Tay Sach's disease or a host of other recessive traits. Consequently, the rubella-exposed woman has much less justification for a therapeutic abortion than most of the clients who come for genetic counseling. This is particularly so since special gamma globulin therapy is effective, if given early. Fortunately, the answer to the rubella problem is conceptually very simple: all girls should be infected with rubella at some time before marriage. This virus produces a long immunity, and it should be isolated and cultured very soon.

Another environmental factor for which fears and fancies have far outrun the facts is anoxia. Anoxia is a natural hazard of childbirth, and in most cases the infant makes a normal adjustment to it. When infants suffer from delayed respiration or asphyxia during birth, it is widely accepted that this is responsible for later difficulties such as convulsions, mental retardation and perhaps other neurologic abnormalities. The early studies were badly biased and were not adequate to prove their contentions. Prospective studies, as with rubella, are necessary to provide useful data.

Schachter and Apgar (1959) did a study of 104 newborn infants with follow-up and psychologic testing in 1956. They found that the group with perinatal complications was impaired on four psychologic tests and five diagnostic signs. They stated: "The positive findings would appear to support previous results showing a significant effect of early asphyxia. However, the clinical significance of the data on the special tests appears to be ambiguous. In addition, the small though statistically significant impairment of 4.9 points in I.Q. for the complicated subjects is of questionable clinical significance."

Even such slight differences as these were not apparent in the extensive study of Keith and Gage (1960). This was a second follow-up on Mayo Clinic children, of whom 80 per cent were between 8 and 14 years of age at the time of follow-up. Their sample started with 402 infants born after prolonged labor, 236 with asphyxia or delayed respiration at birth, 110 survivors whose mothers had toxemia and 633 controls. Other infants had died soon after birth, but this work was concerned only with survivors. If the infants survived, there were no significant differences in neurologic lesions or convulsions between the groups. The I.Q. differences for a 10 per cent sample gave a mean I.Q. of 116.8 for the prolonged labor cases, 117.3 for the asphyxia cases and 114.3 for the controls. These differences were not statistically significant.

Thus, we find the obvious fact that babies can still be suffocated at birth. However, unsuccessful suffocation experiences do not seem to result in permanent damage very often.

It should not be thought that it is impossible to break down the extensive defenses evolution has provided for the embryo. Our problem is to sort out properly designed experiments from those leading off in the wrong direction.

There are numerous instances of severe damage done to embryos in utero, and one of the most specific instances is the recent epidemic of cases of phocomelia in West Germany. An upsurge of cases of this anomaly was clearly correlated with use of a new sleeping pill (Contergan) by women in their second month of pregnancy, when the limbs are formed. The anomaly is called "seal limbs" because the hands and feet are like flippers, attached close to the body with little or no arm or leg. The retrospective aspects of this nightmare are clear enough. It is thought that thalidomide, the drug in Contergan, may have caused malformation in 20 per cent of the embryos when taken during the second month of development. Needless to say, the drug has been withdrawn from the market in West Germany and Britain. Public use had not been permitted in the United States. However, some thalidomide was distributed to physicians for experimental use and some was brought into the country by returning tourists, with the result that at least four cases of phocomelia have been recorded, including a set of deformed twins.

A recent, very public flurry of interest in thalidomide resulted from the suit of Mrs. Sherri Finkbine requesting that the Superior Court of Arizona permit her an abortion because she had taken the drug. A three-member panel of doctors advised the abortion. However, the court dismissed her suit because the laws of Arizona and most other states permit an abortion only if the life of the mother is in peril. It is entirely irrelevant, legally, what the fate of the unborn child may be. Is this mercy?

Epidemics of phocomelia caused by thalidomide can be expected to be extremely infrequent. One should be more concerned with the usual variables in the environment, such as the seasons of the year. Edwards (1961) investigated the month of birth of all congenitally malformed infants born in Birmingham, England, in various years between 1945 and 1956. There seemed to be an excess of anencephaly in January, of harelip in March, of patent ductus arteriosus in July and of congenital dislocation of the hip in January. The differences were not large, when chance fluctuations are eliminated, and would not be expected to be reproduced in all parts of the world. They are probably of little importance compared with uterine differences, which are part of the mother's internal environment. Unfortunately, the mother's internal environment is very difficult to investigate, but it should provide a mass of interesting facts when appropriate research techniques have been devised.

Warburton and Fraser (1959) have emphasized that the development of a fetus depends on a precise and extremely intricate system of interactions between *two* sets of hereditary factors and *two* environments, all acting at the same time on the growing baby. The mother and the fetus each have their own environment and their own genotype. Consequently, the interaction will be complicated in the case of the common congenital malformations.

Fraser (1959) has given much thought to the contribution of environmental factors to the development of congenital anomalies. He concluded that a minority of the common congenital malformations have a major environmental cause and that like-

wise only a minority of them have a major genetic cause. Therefore, most malformations probably result from complicated interactions between genetic predispositions and subtle factors in the
intrauterine environment. There is certainly no one cause and
no one cure for malformations.

In summary, we can agree with Fraser that for any clinical
category of common malformations, it is likely that there will be
a few cases with a simple mendelian genetic cause, a few with
a definite environmental origin and a great majority that result
from complicated interactions between multiple genetic and
environmental factors.

Chapter 29

PUTTING THE PUZZLE TOGETHER

It would be possible to add a practically endless number of chapters to this book. They would be concerned with diseases like progressive muscular dystrophy, hemophilia, retinoblastoma, sickle cell anemia, and many other extremely interesting traits for which the genetic picture is fairly well understood. Such uncommon traits are of supreme importance to genetic theory and the research with them makes fascinating reading. However, the incidence of these intriguing genes in the general population is so low that many a physician will complete his practice without ever seeing many of them among his patients. Consequently, it is necessary, in order to keep the book small, to close without considering very much of the most clear-cut and thoroughly convincing evidence for mendelian heredity in man. It has been our lot to struggle with such complicated traits as schizophrenia, in which the heredity seems to be that of an incomplete dominant with incomplete penetrance. This sounds too incomplete for words, and the impatient soul may decide to toss out the genes altogether. If we had no genes, all of our problems would be solved because we wouldn't exist. This solution is obviously too drastic, as even the protozoa can't divide and flourish without their genes. We are stuck with our heredity and we will have to get along with it as best we may. We may learn how to overrule some genes, and we can favor and increase others, but many will provide us with problems for thousands of generations to come.

Why is it that the traits we have considered, most of which have a frequency of at least 1 affected individual per 1,000 births, show such variability in their expression? Why do they all have an important environmental component? The answer seems to be that the environmental suppression of their effects acts as a disguise and permits *some* of the affected persons to live long enough to produce children. This increases the frequency of the gene over what it would be if such persons had all succumbed at birth to their genetic handicap. Genes that are *invariably* lethal before reproductive age should not reach high frequencies except when they have beneficial effects in their heterozygous condition. Some genes have been shown to have such bizarre dual roles. Genes with mildly deleterious effects can become widespread because they are protected by environmental fluctuations in some proportion of the affected persons. Other individuals who fail to receive environmental protection, and so die without reproducing, will function as eradicators of the undesirable genes. But new mutations of previously normal genes will restore the supply of unwanted genes. Such is life!

The reader may have developed the impression that when twins are studied, there will always be high concordance between the identicals but low concordance between the fraternals. This is generally true for traits with a genetic basis and when the heredity for the trait is not present in the entire populace. It is *not* true when almost everyone does have the same heredity, such as that for susceptibility to measles or some other very common infectious diseases. A comparison of the twin material already given for clubfoot with the data for measles is a good illustration of how distinct the two situations are. The comparison is provided in Table XXVI. Clubfoot, although strongly affected by environmental factors, shows clear evidence of heredity because of the congenital difference between the two types of twins. On the other hand, there is no striking difference between the two types of twins in their susceptibility to measles. If they got the agent, they got the disease; probably almost everyone is genetically susceptible to the infection. This is not the case for all infectious diseases, of course, and some would show sharp differences between identical and fraternal twins.

The twin method is not perfect, but none of our methods in biology and medicine are perfect. Price (1950) has shown that our built-in biases in twin studies result in an *underestimate* of the influence of heredity. The method is not only of great value in itself, but it is, in fact, about the only useful method that we have for the study of *common* disease traits. Ordinarily, we think of the pedigree method as the cornerstone of human genetics, not only because the repetition of affected individuals in the pedigree is good evidence of heredity but also because inspection of several pedigrees should indicate whether the trait is behaving as a dominant or recessive—that is, for uncommon traits. If the trait is common, both of these advantages will be diminished because every large pedigree will be found to contain some affected persons. With a high gene frequency one cannot distinguish readily whether the mating is between a heterozygous dominant and a normal, or between a homozygous recessive and a carrier; both crosses should produce 50 per cent

TABLE XXVI   The Different Pictures for a Hereditary and an Infectious Disease as Shown by Twin Data (Even Though Clubfoot is Only Weakly Hereditary, the Distinction between Its Twin Picture and That for Measles Is clear)

	Both Twins with Clubfoot	One Twin with Clubfoot	Both Twins with Measles	One Twin with Measles
Identical	13 (32%)	27 (68%)	179 (95%)	10 (5%)
Fraternal	4 (3%)	130 (97%)	127 (87%)	19 (13%)

affected persons. These difficulties are demonstrated only too well in the various studies on the genetics of diabetes mellitus.

The consanguinity method also falls down with *all* common traits. If a person carries a gene for a particular characteristic, the chance that his first cousin will carry this same gene is 1 in 8. However, if a recessive anomaly shows an incidence of better than 1 in 1,000 affected persons, the heterozygous condition will be present in better than 1 out of 16 persons. Thus, the increased expectation of affected persons from first cousin marriages is so small that it may be statistically impossible to prove an excess of affected families from matings of first cousins compared with matings of nonrelatives. Böök (1948) has provided a promising new lead in this field by showing that the frequency of clubfoot within affected sibships produced by relatives is greater than that within sibships from nonrelatives. This point should be developed in future studies, as it would shed light where we most need it—on the common disease traits.

There are many other techniques for studying medical genetics that might have been included in this book, were it not for the need to keep it small and easy to read. But before ending the book, it may be well to consider one of the ways in which the physician is likely to affect the population of the future to a great extent.

It is the physician who is likely to have a hand in shaping the future evolution of mankind because our reproduction is no longer completely capricious. The desire for a happy family of normal children is one of the strongest human motivations. For the first time in history the physician is able to be of major assistance in achieving the highest of life's goals. If a couple is sterile, he may help in bringing about fertility. If a couple find that the family is increasing beyond their fondest expectations, he can slow down the flood. In civilized countries responsible parents no longer leave reproduction to the vagaries of chance.

The physician officiates at the birth of the child and is the authoritative source of scientific information about reproduction.

The physician of today not only helps couples achieve a family size appropriate to their environment, but, by means of genetic counseling, he can assist them to approach the quality of children they desire. A couple who had five boys, three doomed to die of progressive muscular dystrophy, succeeded in producing the quantity of children they wanted, but they are most unhappy that three of their children will never become men. The physician of tomorrow will very probably be able to guarantee them five normal boys. At least, he will be able to tell such a mother whether or not she carries the sex-linked gene for pseudohypertrophic muscular dystrophy. This mother had lost a brother with the disease, and the physician of today could have told her that she had an even chance of carrying the gene for the abnormality. Most of the techniques for improving man's genotype are still in the future, but at no time in history have we been in the favorable position that we are in today. The fact that life expectancy has been doubled in a few generations is not due to the faith healer and the quack but to the physician who is using his science with a sense of responsibility that it would be difficult to match. Today his responsibility includes helping couples with their problems of heredity and reproduction.

The point that is being approached is this. In the United States today practically all fertile couples know that they can regulate their family size to a considerable degree by using either the rhythm method or contraceptives. A good proportion of them also know that something can be done to avoid the appearance of abnormal children, whether the abnormality be due to environmental or genetic factors or both. Obviously, they are going to ask the physician for answers to their questions. The time has come when the physician can give correct answers to a large number of these serious pleas for knowledge.

Each question is likely to be different from the others, and each is a different puzzle. The physician must put a number of pieces together in order to solve the problem. The best that the geneticist can do is to supply some of the pieces of the puzzle. In the last analysis, it is the physician who will have to fit the pieces together. In the puzzle will be pieces supplied by biochemistry, economics, religion, social class concepts, medicine, genetics and, most important of all, common sense.

The geneticist can supply the essential data, but he has no real rapport with the couple. He is not a part of the family and cannot decide whether or not the couple should try to have more or fewer children, depending upon the genetic problem being faced. The family physician is in a better position. He is the medical and biologic advisor to the family, and the members want him to help them in making their decisions regarding their own reproduction. How much assistance can be given depends upon the always slightly different pieces of the puzzles that have to be fitted together.

Life would be intellectually simpler if we could abolish all science. We could suppress nuclear physics as we once outlawed the crossbow. But as long as man has his brains, we can't completely stifle his curiosity about himself and the world around him. It looks as if science and the physician are here to stay. We have passed the point of no return.

The practice of medicine is often referred to as an art, but it is an art that must be restricted to scientists. The physician is the chief scientist with whom the ordinary family has personal contact. It may come as something of a shock to the physician to realize that man's future evolution rests upon the doctor's ability and judgment. Man's evolution depends upon changes in his heredity. There will be no appreciable change in the genotype of the species in one year, nor will one physician cause much variation of the genes. However, over the millennia there will be changes, and they must come at the family level, where the doctor functions.

It has been pointed out earlier that the discovery of insulin was dysgenic in that it permitted those with the heredity for diabetes to live and increase the incidence of the deleterious gene over what it would have been had they died, as was usual in the past. This type of evolution has occurred and will become even more frequent as the genes for one disease after another are overruled by medical advances. We will eventually, as a species, be carrying a heavy load of defective heredity, which we will patch up with false teeth and artificial organs of every description. This won't happen overnight. The speed at which it comes about will result in large part from the success of medical research balanced by the quality of genetic counseling provided by the physician. It seems probable that our evolution in the future will be much more rapid than it has been in the past.

There isn't any question that our *immediate* social advances or calamities will depend upon other factors than gene changes. It is the gene changes over periods of thousands of years that will gradually become the responsibility of the medical profession. At present one of the physician's major responsibilities is to learn how to ensure a family of happy normal children for each couple. Even for this immediate obligation there is still much to be learned. It is hoped that this book contains a few bits and pieces to help solve some of today's counseling problems in medical genetics.

Appendix

THE RARE GENETIC

TRAITS

The body of this book has been restricted to traits appearing in one or more individuals out of about every 1,000 born. The geneticist considers these traits to be "common" and realizes that for any common genetic trait that is deleterious there will be usually more than one pair of genes involved, with environmental modifiers having an effect as well. With the common traits, such as diabetes, there may be heterogeneity both of the clinical forms of the disease and of the genetics involved. However, the empiric risk figures for diabetes at least simulate recessive inheritance. The client should be instructed as to what the empiric risk figures are and what they mean. The client can also be told that diabetes appears to behave as if determined by recessive inheritance. This is an appropriate explanation in the present state of our knowledge and should not have any unfortunate consequences. It is possible that the average client can understand how recessive heredity works. Complicated polygenic systems would certainly be beyond the comprehension of most clients and should merely be described as an hereditary tendency. Perhaps it would be best in counseling with the common traits to simply state that there is an hereditary basis for the disease, and to state the average chance of an appearance of the trait in the relevant situation. The client is more interested in a practical risk figure than in the exact genetic mechanism involved.

One might think that counseling would be absolutely precise for the rare recessive traits. However, a trait may behave as an ordinary recessive in one pedigree, as a sex-linked recessive in a second pedigree and as a dominant in still a different family group.

In the first edition of this book, Dr. Clarke Fraser's list of rare traits, their type of heredity and frequency of expression was reproduced. Perhaps such a list makes life too simple for the physician. If it is stated that a trait behaves as a sex-linked recessive, the physician may fail to notice that in the client's family there is an affected girl. This probably indicates that his client should be concerned with ordinary recessive inheritance rather than the sex-linked type. The consequences are quite different in subsequent generations for the two types of inheritance. Therefore, because of the ease of confusion, it seems reasonable to expect the physician to do one of three things. (1) He may refer the client to the nearest genetic counselor. Some of them are listed in this book. (2) He may do nothing at all, that is, state that he doesn't know the answer to the client's question. (3) He may go to the literature and learn what is known about the heredity of the trait.

The new listing of traits with a reference for each is in accord with the philosophy given above. Bluntly stated, if a physician wishes to do genetic counseling, he should have some acquaintance with the genetic literature concerned with the trait. The reference given will usually be the most recent one known to me in 1962, but it may not be the best one on the subject. However, it will permit going back to the most important paper without difficulty. There isn't any short cut to the acquisition of knowledge, but these references may expedite the process. Human genetics has become so elaborate that a single word description of a trait as "recessive" is no longer adequate, in many cases.

Some of the publications listed have small circulations. Most university libraries will have all the publications cited. The county medical association library can obtain a photostatic copy of the article for permanent retention. The value of reading at least one definitive article on the trait of interest can hardly be overemphasized. It will not only be useful for genetic counseling, but it might also result in a different diagnosis for the person involved.

Even though this list of rare traits seems to be almost endless, it does not include all those known. If the reader fails to find a reference here to the trait of interest he should continue his search elsewhere. The heredity of more traits is known for man than for any other organism. The compilation of a complete list of them would be beyond the limits of practicality.

The writer has made extensive use of Dr. V. A. McKusick's *Medical Genetics* 1958–1960, published by the C. V. Mosby Company, St. Louis. It is a most useful compilation of abstracts of recent papers in human genetics. One can hardly be grateful enough to him for the heroic labor involved in preparing his volume of almost 1000 abstracts. The abstracts for 1961 papers have been published in the May, 1962, issue of the *Journal of Chronic Diseases.*

TRAIT	REFERENCE
Abetalipoproteinemia.	Salt, H. B. et al. On having no beta-lipoprotein. Lancet *ii:* 325, 1960.
Acanthocytosis.	See *Abetalipoproteinemia.*
Acanthosis nigricans.	Curth, H. O. and B. M. Aschner. Genetic studies on acanthosis nigricans. A.M.A. Arch. Dermat. 79:55, 1959.

TRAIT   REFERENCE

Acatalasemia.   Nishimura, E. T. et al. Carrier state in human
                               acatalasemia. Science *130:*333, 1959.

Achondroplasia.   Lamy, M., P. Maroteaux and J. Frézal. Les chon-
                               drodystrophies genotypiques. Semaine hôp. Paris
                               *34:*1675, 1958.

Acrocephalosyndactyly   Blank, C. E. Apert's syndrome (a type of acroce-
    (Apert's syndrome).   phalosyndactyly). Ann. Hum. Genet. (London)
                               *24:*151, 1960.

Adrenal cortical hypoplasia.   Boyd, J. F. and A. M. MacDonald. Adrenal cortical
                               hypoplasia in siblings. Arch. Dis. Childh. *35:*561,
                               1960.

Adrenal hyperplasia.   Klevit, H. D. Congenital virilizing adrenal hyper-
                               plasia. A.M.A. J. Dis. Child. *100:*415, 1960.

Agammaglobulinemia.   Fudenberg, H. et al. The occurrence of rheumatoid
                               factor and other gammaglobulin abnormalities in
                               the families of patients with agammaglobulinemia.
                               J. Clin. Invest. *39:*987, 1960.

Albinism.   Froggatt, P. Albinism in Northern Ireland. Ann.
                               Hum. Genet. (London) *24:*213, 1960.

Alder anomaly.   François J. et al. Les conducteurs du gène de l'atro-
                               phia gyrata chorioideae et retinae de Fuchs (ano-
                               malie d'Alder). Acta genet. med. gemell. *9:*74, 1960.

Aldrich's syndrome.   Motulsky, A. G. Mutations and sex-linked throm-
                               bocytopenia. Lancet *ii:*1449, 1960.

Aleukia with reticular   DeVaal, O. M. and V. Seynhaeve. Reticular dys-
    dysgenesis.   genesis. Lancet *ii:*1123, 1959.

Alkaptonuria.   Abe, Y. et al. Thirteen cases of alkaptonuria from
                               one family tree with special reference to osteo-
                               arthrosis alkaptonuria. J. Bone & Joint Surg. *42A:*
                               817, 1960.

Alopecia areata.   Lubowe, I. I. The clinical aspects of alopecia areata,
                               totalis and universalis. Ann. New York Acad. Sci.
                               *183:*458, 1959.

Alopecia congenita.   Stevanovic, D. V. Alopecia congenita. Acta genet.
                               et statis. med. (Basel) *9:*127, 1959.

Alzheimer's disease.   Wheelen, L. and R. R. Race. Familial Alzheimer's
                               disease; with a note on the linkage data. Ann. Hum.
                               Genet. (London) *23:*300, 1959.

TRAIT	REFERENCE

Amaurotic idiocy.

Aronson, S. M. and B. W. Volk. Cerebral Sphingo-lipidoses. Chapter 27. New York Academic Press, 1962.

Amblyopia.

Cole, R. B. W. The problem of unilateral ambly-opia. Brit. Med. J. *1:*202, 1959.

Amputations (congenital).

Birch-Jensen, A. Congenital deformities of the up-per extremities. Opera ex domo biol. hum. hered. (Copenhagen) vol. 19, 1949.

Amyotrophic lateral sclerosis.

Espinosa, et al. Hereditary amyotrophic lateral sclerosis. Neurology *12:*7, 1962.

Angiokeratoma corporis diffusum.

Rahman, A. N. et al. Angiokeratoma corporis dif-fusum universale (hereditary dystopic lipidosis). Tr. A. Am. Physicians *74:*366, 1961.

Angioneurotic edema.

Trigg, J. W. Hereditary angioneurotic edema. New England J. Med. *264:*761, 1961.

Anhidrotic ectodermal dysplasia.

Awwaad, S. and M. El-Essawy. Hereditary anhi-drotic ectodermal dysplasia. Arch. Pediat. *77:*496, 1960.

Aniridia.

Shaw, M. W. et al. Congenital aniridia. Am. J. Hum. Genet. *12:*389, 1960.

Ankylosing spondylitis.

Kornstad, A. M. G. and L. Kornstad. Ankylosing spondylitis in two families showing involvement of female members only. Acta rheum. scand. *6:*59, 1960.

Aortic stenosis.

Reynolds, J. L. et al. Critical congenital aortic ste-nosis with minimal electrocardiographic changes. New England J. Med. *262:*276, 1960.

Arcus corneae (arcus senilis).

Ahuja, Y. R. L'hérédité de l'arcus corneae. J. génét. hum. (Geneva) *8:*95, 1959.

Arginosuccinuria.

Westfall, R. G. Arginosuccinicaciduria: identifica-tion of the metabolic defect in a newly described form of mental deficiency. Proc. IV Internat. Con-gress Biochem. Section 13–34, p. 168. Vienna, 1958.

Arthrogryposis.

Frischknecht, W. et al. Familiäre arthrogryposis multiplex congenita. Helvet. paediat. acta *15:*259, 1960.

TRAIT

TRAIT	REFERENCE
Ataxia-Telangiectasia syndrome.	Sedgwick, R. P. and E. Boder. Progressive ataxia in childhood with particular reference to ataxia-telangiectasia. Neurology *10:*705, 1960.
Atrophodermia vermiculata.	Kooij, R. and J. Venter. Atrophodermia vermiculata with unusual localisation and associated congenital anomalies. Dermatologica *118:*161, 1959.
B-amino-isobutyric acid excretion.	McEvoy-Bowe, E. Family studies of urinary B-amino-isobutyric acid excretion together with an examination of the urinary excretion levels of glycine, alanine, taurine and glutamine among Chinese in Singapore. Ann. Hum. Genet. (London) 25:331–341.
Black blood disease.	Tamura, A. et al. A study on the hereditary black blood disease (Nigremia hereditaria). Jap. J. Hum. Genet. *4:*180, 1959.
"Blue-Rubber-Bleb" nevus disease (cavernous hemangiomatosis).	Berlyne, G. M. and N. Berlyne. Anaemia due to "Blue-Rubber-Bleb" nevus disease. Lancet *ii:*1275, 1960.
Branchial cysts.	Wheeler, C. E. et al. Branchial anomalies in three generations of one family. A.M.A. Arch. Dermat. 77:715, 1958.
Cardiomegaly (familial).	Schiebler, G. L. et al. Familial cardiomegaly in association with the Wolff-Parkinson-White syndrome. Am. Heart J. *58:*113, 1959.
Cardiomyopathy (familial).	Hollman, A. et al. A family with obstructive cardiomyopathy (asymmetrical hypertrophy). Brit. Heart J. 22:449, 1960.
Cataract.	Waardenburg, P. J. et al. Genetics and Ophthalmology. Chapter 12. Springfield, Illinois, Charles C Thomas, 1961.
Catlin marks.	Kite, W. C. Seizures associated with the Catlin mark. Neurology *11:*345, 1961.
Celiac syndrome.	Carter, C. O. et al. The inheritance of coeliac disease. Ann. Hum. Genet. (London) *23:*266, 1959.
Cerebellar degeneration.	Aagenaes, O. Hereditary spastic paraplegia. Acta psychiat. neurol. scand. *34:*489, 1959.
Charcot-Marie-Tooth syndrome.	Norstrand, I. F. and M. E. Margulies. Peripheral neuronopathy (Charcot-Marie-Tooth) in association with gastrointestinal symptoms. New York. J. Med. 58:863, 1958.

TRAIT	REFERENCE
Chediak-Higashi syndrome.	Undritz, E. Morphology and genetics in hereditary constitutional anomalies of leukocytes. Acta haemat. *24:*59, 1960.
Cherubism (familial fibrous dysplasia of the jaws).	Thompson, N. Cherubism: familial fibrous dysplasia of the jaws. Brit. J. Plast. Surg. *12:*89, 1959.
Chondrodystrophia congenita punctata (Conradi's disease).	Allansmith, M. and E. Senz. Chrondrodystrophia congenita punctata. A.M.A.J. Dis. Child. *100:*109, 1960.
Chorioretinal atrophy.	See *Alder's anomaly.*
Choroideremia.	Pameyer, J. K. et al. Choroideremia. Brit. J. Ophthal. *44:*724, 1960.
Christmas disease.	Ikkala, E. Haemophilia. Scand. J. Clin. Lab. Invest. *12:* suppl. 46, 1960.
Cleidocranial dysostosis.	Thoms, J. Cleidocranial dysostosis; report of two cases with special characteristics. Acta radiol. *50:* 514, 1958.
Cockayne's syndrome (similar to but different from Gilford's progeria).	Macdonald, W. B. et al. Cockayne's syndrome: an heredo-familial disorder of growth and development. Pediatrics *25:*997, 1960.
Cooley's disease.	Artese, D. Genetics of Cooley's disease. Arch. pat. clin. med. *37:*330–344, 1961.
Color blindness.	Whittaker, D. L. et al. Linkage of color blindness to hemophilias A and B. Am. J. Hum. Genet. *14:*149–158, 1962.
Craniofacial dysostosis.	Gorlin, R. J. et al. Craniofacial dysostosis, patent ductus arteriosus, hypertrichosis, hypoplasia of labia majora, dental and eye anomalies—a new syndrome. J. Pediat. *56:*778, 1960.
Craniometaphyseal dysplasia.	Schwartz, E. Craniometaphyseal dysplasia. Am. J. Roentgenol. *84:*461, 1960.
Craniostenosis (as distinct from Crouzon's and Apert's syndromes).	Gordon, H. Craniostenosis. Brit. Med. J. *2:*792, 1959.
Crigler-Najjar syndrome.	Childs, B. et al. Glucuronic acid conjugation by patients with familial nonhemolytic jaundice and their relatives. Pediatrics *23:*903, 1959.

TRAIT	REFERENCE
Crouzon's disease.	Dodge, H. W., Jr. et al. Craniofacial dysostosis. Pediatrics 23:98, 1959.
Cutis laxa (as distinct from the Ehlers-Danlos syndrome).	Sestak, Z. Ehlers-Danlos syndrome and cutis laxa: an account of families in the Oxford area. Ann. Hum. Genet. (London) 25:313–321, 1962.
Cystathioninuria.	Harris, H. et al. Cystathioninuria. Ann. Hum. Genet. (London) 23:442, 1959.
Cystinosis (Lignac-de Toni-Fanconi syndrome).	Garron, L. K. Cystinosis. Tr. Am. Acad. Ophthal. 63:99, 1959.
Cystinuria.	Knox, W. E. Sir Archibald Garrod's "Inborn Errors of Metabolism" I. Cystinuria. Am. J. Hum. Gen. 10:3, 1958.
Dandy-Walker syndrome.	Brodal, A. and E. Hauglie-Hanssen. Congenital hydrocephalus with defective development of the cerebellar vermis (Dandy-Walker syndrome). J. Neurol. Neurosurg. Psychiat. 22:99, 1959.
Darier-White's disease.	Witcop, C. J. and R. J. Gorlin. Four hereditary mucosal syndromes. Arch. Dermat. 84:762, 1961.
Deafness.	Deraemaeker, R. Recessive congenital deafness in a North Belgian province. Acta genet. et stat. med. (Basel) 10:295, 1960.
Dentinogenesis imperfecta.	Johnson, O. N. Hereditary dentinogenesis imperfecta. J. Pediat. 54:6, 1959.
Diabetes insipidus.	Wenzl, J. E. et al. Clinics on endocrine and metabolic diseases. 6. Nephrogenic diabetes insipidus. Proc. Mayo Clin. 36:543, 1961.
Diaphysial aclasis.	Krooth, R. S., M. T. Macklin and T. F. Hilbish. Diaphysial aclasis on Guam. Am. J. Hum. Gen. 13:340–347, 1961.
Dislocation of the patella and shoulder (recurrent).	Carter, C. and R. Sweetnam. Recurrent dislocation of the patella and shoulder. J. Bone & Joint Surg. 42B:721, 1961.
Disseminated sclerosis.	Refsum, S. Possible genetic factors in disseminated sclerosis. Proc. Roy. Soc. Med. 54:35, 1961.

TRAIT	REFERENCE
Dubin-Johnson syndrome (hyperbilirubinemia).	Berkowitz, D. et al. Dubin-Johnson syndrome: report of a case occurring in a Negro male. New England J. Med. *262*:1028, 1960.
Dwarfism (birdheaded).	Seckel, H. P. G. Bird-Headed Dwarfs. Springfield, Illinois, Charles C Thomas Co., 1960.
Dysautonomia.	McKendrick, T. Familial dysautonomia. Arch. Dis. Childh. *33:*465, 1958.
Dyschromatosis symmetrica.	Ishikuni, N. et al. Hosojima. Am. J. Hum. Genet. *12:*67–75, 1960.
Dyskeratosis (benign intraepithelial).	Witkop, C. J. et al. Hereditary benign intraepithelial dyskeratosis. A.M.A. Arch. Path. *70*:696, 1960.
Dysostosis (metaphyseal).	Daeschner, C. W. et al. Metaphyseal dysostosis. J. Pediat. *57:*844, 1960.
Dystonia musculorum deformans.	Zeman, W. et al. Idiopathic dystonia musculorum deformans. Neurology *10:*1068, 1960.
Dystrophia myotonica.	Dumaine, L. and P. Lozeron. Contribution a l'étude clinique et génétique de la dystrophie congénitale (Thomsen). J. génét. hum. (Geneva) *10:*221–296, 1961.
Ectodermal dysplasia.	Mohler, D. N. Hereditary ectodermal dysplasia of the anhidrotic type associated with primary hypogonadism. Am. J. Med. *27:*682, 1959.
Ectopia lentis et pupillae.	Walles, G. L. and G. G. Heath. Dominant ectopia lentis et pupillae. Am. J. Hum. Genet. *11:*166, 1959.
Ectrodactyly (lobster claw).	Stevenson, A. C. and L. M. Jennings. Ectrodactyly—evidence in favour of a disturbed segregation in the offspring of affected males. Ann. Hum. Genet. (London) *24:*89, 1960.
Ehlers-Danlos syndrome.	McKusick, V. Heritable Disorders of Connective Tissue. 2nd ed. St. Louis, C. V. Mosby Company, 1960.
Elliptocytosis (ovalocytosis).	Clarke, C. A. et al. Data on linkage in man: ovalocytosis, sickling, and the rhesus blood group complex. Ann. Hum. Genet. (London) *24:*283–287, 1960.
Ellis–van Creveld syndrome (chondroectodermal dysplasia).	Walls, W. L. et al. Chondroectodermal dysplasia. A.M.A.J. Dis. Child. *98:*242, 1959.

TRAIT	REFERENCE
Enamel dysplasia (amelogenesis imperfecta).	Chaudhry, A. P. Hereditary enamel dysplasia. J. Pediat. *54:*776, 1959.
Enamel hypoplasia.	Tsuju, T. and M. Obi. A family of hereditary enamel hypoplasia. Jap. J. Hum. Genet. *6:*118, 1961.
Encephalopathy (progressive).	Liu, M. C. and P. E. Sylvester. Familial diffuse progressive encephalopathy. Arch. Dis. Childh. *35:*345, 1960.
Engelmann's disease.	Lennan, E. A. et al. Engelmann's disease. J. Bone & Joint Surg. *43B:*273, 1961.
Epidermolysis bullosa.	Readett, M. D. Localized epidermolysis bullosa. Brit. Med. J. *1:*1514, 1961.
Epidermolysis bullosa simplex.	Klunker, W. Un arbre genealogique d'une famille atteinte d'epidermolyse bulleuse simple (Köbner). J. génét. hum. (Geneva) *8:*72–75, 1959.
Epiloia.	Stevenson, A. C. and O. D. Fisher. Frequency of epiloia in Northern Ireland. Brit. J. Prev. Soc. Med. *10:*134–135, 1956.
Epiphyseal dysplasia.	Leeds, N. E. Epiphyseal dysplasia multiplex. Am. J. Roentgenol. *84:*506, 1960.
Erythrokeratoderma figurata.	Saul, A. Eritroqueratodermia figurada en placas congenita y familiar. Dermat. rev. mex. *4:*40, 1960.
Eyelids (laxity).	Levitt, J. M. Hereditary changes in skin of the eyelids. A.M.A. Arch. Ophthal. *62:*506, 1959.
Factors I through IX (blood).	Wright, I. S. Nomenclature of blood clotting factors. J.A.M.A. *170:*325, 1959.
Fanconi's anemia.	Nilsson, L. R. and G. Lundholm. Congenital thrombocytopenia associated with aplasia of the radius. Acta paediat. *49:*291, 1960.
Favism.	See *Glucose-6-phosphate dehydrogenase deficiency.*
Fetal hemoglobin (persistent).	Bradley, T. B., Jr. and C. L. Conley. Studies of an inherited disorder manifested by persistence of fetal hemoglobin. Tr. A. Am. Physicians *73:*72, 1960.
Fox-Fordyce disease.	Graham, J. H. et al. Fox-Fordyce disease in male identical twins. A.M.A. Arch. Dermat. *82:*212, 1960.

TRAIT	REFERENCE
Franceschetti's syndrome (Treacher-Collins).	Monnet, P. et al. Deux cas de dysostose mandibulo-faciale ou syndrome de Franceschetti. Pédiatrie *15:* 537, 1960.
Friedreich's ataxia.	Powell, E. D. U. Blood-group studies in Friedreich's ataxia. Brit. Med. J. *1:*868, 1961.
Fructose intolerance (as distinct from benign fructosuria).	Prader, A. et al. Hereditary fructose intolerance. Maandschr. Kindergeneeskunde *28:*47–50, 1960.
Fuch's atrophy.	See *Alder anomaly.*
Galactosemia.	Walker, F. A. et al. Galactosemia: a study of 27 kindreds in North America. Ann. Hum. Gen. (London) *25:*287–311, 1962.
Gamma globulin.	Grubb, R. Hereditary gamma globulin groups in man. Am. J. Hum. Genet. *13:*171–174, 1961.
Gardner's syndrome.	Kelly, P. B. and D. A. McKinnon. Familial multiple polyposis of the colon. McGill Med. J. *30:*67, 1961.
Gaucher's disease.	Hsia, D. Y-Y. et al. Gaucher's disease: report of two cases in father and son and review of the literature. New England J. Med. *261:*164, 1959.
Gargoylism (Hurler's syndrome).	Mittwoch, U. Cytological and biochemical studies on gargoylism. Ann. Hum. Gen. (London) *25:*424, 1962.
Giant neutrophil leucocytes.	Davidson, W. M. et al. Giant neutrophil leucocytes: an inherited anomaly. Brit. J. Haemat. *6:*339, 1960.
Giant urticaria.	Cohen, J. D. Chronic familial giant urticaria. Ann. Intern. Med. *54:*331, 1961.
Gilbert's disease (hyperbilirubinemia).	Beker, S. and A. E. Read. Familial Dubin-Johnson syndrome. Gastroenterology *35:*387, 1958.
Glanzmann-Naegeli disease.	Gross, R. et al. Über die Natur der Thrombasthenie Thrombopathie Glanzmann-Naegeli. Klin. Wschr. *38:*193, 1960.
Glaucoma (congenital).	Barkan, O. and W. J. Ferguson, Jr. Congenital glaucoma. Pediat. Clin. North America, p. 225, Feb. 1958.
Glioma.	Van der Wiel, H. J. Inheritance of Glioma: The Genetic Aspects of Cerebral Glioma and Its Rela-

tion to Status Dysraphicus. New York, D. Van Nostrand Co., Inc., 1960.

Glomus tumors.

Gorlin, R. J. et al. Multiple glomus tumor of the pseudocavernous hemangioma type. A.M.A. Arch. Dermat. *82:*776, 1960.

Glucose-6-phosphate dehydrogenase deficiency.

Porter, I. H. et al. Genetical linkage between the loci for glucose-6-phosphate dehydrogenase deficiency and colour-blindness in American Negroes. Ann. Hum. Genet. (London) *26:*107–122, 1962.

Glycogen storage disease.

Illingworth, B. Glycogen storage disease. Am. J. Clin. Nutr. *9:*683–690, 1961.

Gout.

Duncan, H. and A. St. J. Dixon. Gout, familial hyperuricaemia, and renal disease. Quart J. Med. *29:*129, 1960.

Hageman factor.

Thompson, J. H., Jr. et al. Laboratory and genetic observations in another family with the Hageman trait. Proc. Mayo Clin. *35:*421, 1960.

Hamman-Rich syndrome.

Donohue, W. L. et al. Familial fibrocystic pulmonary dysplasia and its relation to the Hamman-Rich syndrome. Pediatrics *24:*786, 1959.

Hartnup disease.

Milne, M. D. et al. The metabolic disorder in Hartnup disease. Quart. J. Med. *29:*407, 1960.

Hashimoto's disease (struma lymphomatosa).

Dunning, E. J. Struma lymphomatosa: 3 cases in one family. J. Clin. Endocrinol. *19:*1121, 1959.

Hemochromatosis.

Bothwell, T. H. et al. A familial study in idiopathic hemochromatosis. Am. J. Med. *27:*730, 1959.

Hemoglobins S and C.

McCurdy, P. R. and H. A. Pearson. Genetic study of a family possessing hemoglobins S and C, and classical thalassemia. Am. J. Hum. Gen. *13:*390–395, 1961.

Hemolytic anemia (nonspherocytic).

deGruchy, G. C. et al. Nonspherocytic congenital hemolytic anemia. Blood *16:*1371, 1960.

Hemophilia.

Quick, A. J. Hereditary bleeding diseases. J.A.M.A. *178:*941, 1961.

Henoch-Schönlein purpura.

Towner, C. H. Familial incidence of Henoch-Schönlein syndrome. Brit. Med. J. *2:*1385, 1959.

TRAIT	REFERENCE
Hepatic fibrosis.	Kerr, D. N. S. et al. Congenital hepatic fibrosis. Quart. J. Med. *30*:91, 1961.
Hepatolenticular degeneration.	See *Wilson's disease.*
Hirschsprung's disease.	Althoff, W. Zur Genetik der Hirschsprungschen Krankheit. Z. menschl. Vererb. u. Konstitutions lehre *36*:314–340, 1962.
Horner's syndrome.	Durham, D. G. Congenital hereditary Horner's syndrome. A.M.A. Arch. Ophthal. *60*:939, 1958.
Huntington's chorea.	Chandler, J. H. et al. Huntington's chorea in Michigan. Neurology *10*:148, 1960.
Hurler syndrome.	See *Gargoylism.*
Hydatidiform mole.	Edmonds, H. W. Genesis of hydatidiform mole: old and new concepts. Ann. New York Acad. Sci. *80*: 86–99, 1959.
Hypercholesterolemia.	McCleary, J. Primary xanthoma tuberosum in children (with classification of xanthomas). Pediatrics *23*:67, 1959.
Hyperglycinemia.	Childs, B. et al. Idiopathic hyperglycinemia and hyperglycinuria: a new disorder of amino acid metabolism. Pediatrics *27*:522–550, 1961.
Hyperlipemia.	Havel, R. J. and R. S. Gordon, Jr. Idiopathic hyperlipemia: metabolic studies in an affected family. J. Clin. Invest. *39*:1777, 1960.
Hypernephroma.	Brinton, L. F. Hypernephroma-familial occurrence in one family. J.A.M.A. *173*:888, 1960.
Hyperprolinemia.	Scriver, C. R. et al. Evidence for a renal tubular amino acid transport system and a new hereditary disorder of amino acid metabolism. Nature (London) *192*:672, 1961.
Hypogonadism (male).	Nowakowski, H. and W. Lenz. Genetic aspects in male hypogonadism. Recent Prog. Hormone Res. *17*:53, 1961.
Hypophosphatasia.	Rathbun, J. C. et al. Hypophosphatasia: a genetic study. Arch. Dis. Childh. *36*:540, 1961.

TRAIT   REFERENCE

Hypophosphatemia (vitamin-D resistant rickets).

Prader, A. et al. Eine besondere Form der primären Vitamin-D-resistenten Rachitis mit Hypocalcömie und autosomal-dominantem Erbgang: Die hereditäre Pseudo-Mangelrachitis. Helv. paediat. acta *16*:452, 1961.

Hypoplastic anemia.

Diamond, L. K. et al. Congenital (erythroid) hypoplastic anemia. Am. J. Dis. Child. *102*:403, 1961.

Hypothyroidism.

Blizzard, R. M. Inherited defects of thyroid hormone synthesis and metabolism. Metabolism *9*:232, 1960.

Hypovitaminosis-A.

Anderson, I. F. and G. K. Klintworth. Hypovitaminosis-A in a family with tylosis and clinodactyly. Brit. Med. J. *1*:1293, 1961.

Ichthyosis.

Lynch, H. T. et al. Secondary male hypogonadism and congenital ichthyosis: Association of two rare genetic diseases. Am. J. Hum. Genet. *12*:440, 1960.

Incontinentia pigmenti Bloch-Siemens.

Pfeiffer, R. Zur Frage der Vererbung der Incontinentia pigmenti Bloch-Siemens. Z. menschl. Vererb. Konstitutionsl. *35*:469–493, 1960.

Intermittent tetanus.

Forssman, H. Hereditary disorder characterized by attacks of muscular contractions induced by alcohol amongst other factors. Acta med. scand. *170*:517, 1961.

Intestinal polyposis.

Bartholomew, L. G. et al. Intestinal polyposis associated with mucocutaneous pigmentation. Surg. Gynec. Obstet. *115*:1–11, 1962.

Juvenile cerebral lipoidosis (Spielmeyer-Vogt).

Meyer, H. and G. C. Manning. Juvenile cerebral lipoidosis in two siblings. Arch. Neurol. (Chicago) *4*:430, 1961.

Kaposi's sarcoma.

Zeligman, I. Kaposi's sarcoma in a father and son. Bull. Johns Hopkins Hosp. *107*:208, 1960.

Kartagener's syndrome.

Cook, C. D. et al. Blood grouping in three families with Kartagener's syndrome. Am. J. Hum. Genet. *14*:290–294, 1962.

Keratoconus.

Franceschetti, A. et al. Zwei eineiige Zwillingspaare mit konkordantem Keratoconus. Klin. Monatsbl. Augenheilk. *133*:15–30, 1958.

TRAIT	REFERENCE
Keratoconus posticus circumscriptus.	Haney, W. P. and F. Falls. The occurrence of congenital keratoconus posticus circumscriptus. Am. J. Ophthal. *52*:53–57, 1961.
Keratosis palmaris et plantaris (tylosis).	Howel-Evans, W. et al. Carcinoma of the oesophagus with keratosis palmaris et plantaris (tylosis). Quart. J. Med. (N.S.) *27*:413, 1958.
Klinefelter syndrome.	Harnden, D. G. et al. The Klinefelter-Mongolism type of double aneuploidy. Ann. Hum. Genet. (London) *24*:165, 1960.
Kuru.	Bennett, J. H. Population and family studies on kuru. Eugen. Quart. *9*:59–68, 1962.
Lactose disease.	Weijers, H. A. et al. Diarrhoea caused by deficiency of sugar splitting enzymes. Lancet *ii*:296, 1960.
Laurence-Moon-Bardet-Biedl syndrome.	van Bogaert, L. and J. Hariga. La maladie de Bardet-Biedl accompagnée de troubles neurologiques. J. génét. hum. (Geneva) *10*:347–369, 1961.
Leber's amaurosis congenita.	Schappert-Kimmijser, J. et al. Amaurosis congenita (Leber). A.M.A. Arch. Ophthal. *61*:211, 1959.
Leber's optic atrophy.	Kjer, P. Infantile optic atrophy with dominant mode of inheritance. Opera ex domo biol. hum. hered. univ. hafn. (Copenhagen) *42*:146, 1959.
Legg-Calve-Perthes disease.	Wansbrough, R. M. et al. Coxa plana, its genetic aspects and results of treatment with Long-Taylor Walking Caliper. J. Bone & Joint Surg. *41A*:135, 1959.
Leiomyoma (skin).	Kloepfer, H. W. et al. Hereditary multiple leiomyoma of the skin. Am. J. Hum. Genet. *10*:48–52, 1958.
Leprosy.	Belknap, H. R. and W. G. Hayes. A genetic analysis of families in which leprosy occurs. Bull. Tulane Med. Fac. *19*:236, 1960.
Leri's pleonosteosis.	Lane, J. W. Roentogenographic manifestations of the cartilaginous dysplasias. Am. J. Med. Sci. *240*:636, 1960.
Leukodystrophy.	Jervis, G. A. Infantile metachromatic leukodystrophy (Greenfield's disease). J. Neuropath. Exp. Neurol. *19*:323, 1960.

TRAIT | REFERENCE

Leukemia.

Wahrman et al. Manifold chromosome abnormalities in leukemia. Lancet *i*:1098–1100, 1962.

Leukonychia totalis.

Medansky, R. S. and J. M. Fox. Hereditary leukonychia totalis. A.M.A. Arch. Dermat. *82*:412, 1960.

Lipomatosis (multiple).

Stephens, F. E. and A. Isaacson. Hereditary multiple lipomatosis. J. Hered. *50*:51, 1959.

Louis-Bar syndrome.

Sedgwick, R. P. and E. Boder. Progressive ataxia in childhood with particular reference to ataxia-telangiectasia. Neurology *10*:705, 1960.

Lowe's syndrome.

Lowe, C. U. Oculo-cerebral-renal syndrome. Maandschr. Kindergeneesk. *28*:77, 1960.

Lupus erythematosus (systemic).

Marlow, A. A. et al. Familial occurrence of systemic lupus erythematosus. J.A.M.A. *173*:1641, 1960.

Lymphohistiocytic infiltration.

Nelson, P. et al. Generalized lymphohistiocytic infiltration. A familial disease not previously described and different from Letterer-Sive disease and Chediak-Higaski syndrome. Pediatrics *27*:931, 1961.

Macular degeneration.

See *Tapeto-retinal degeneration.*

Macroglobulinemia.

Bayrd, E. D. Continuous chlorambucil therapy in primary macroglobulinemia of Waldenström. Proc. Mayo Clin. *36*:136–147, 1961.

Mandibulofacial dysostosis.

See *Franceschetti's syndrome.*

Maple-syrup urine disease.

Norton, P. M. et al. A new finding in maple-syrup urine disease. Lancet *i*:26, 1962.

Marfan's syndrome.

Sinclair, R. J. G. et al. The Marfan syndrome. Quart. J. Med. *29*:19, 1960.

Marie's cerebellar ataxia.

Matson, G. A. et al. Hereditary ataxia. Ann. Hum. Genet. (London) *25*:7, 1961.

Maxillo-facial dysostosis.

Peters, A. and O. Hövels. Die Dysostosis maxillo-facialis, eine erbliche, typische Fehlbildung des 1. Vsiceralbogens. Z. menschl. Vererb. Konstitutionsl. *35*:434, 1960.

McArdle's syndrome.

Schmid, R. and L. Hammaker. Hereditary absence of muscle phosphorylase (McArdle's syndrome). New England J. Med. *264*:223, 1961.

TRAIT	REFERENCE
Mediterranean fever.	Sohar, E. et al. Genetics of familial Mediterranean fever (FMF). Arch. Intern. Med. *107*:539, 1961.
Metaphysial dysplasia.	David, J. E. A. and P. E. S. Palmer. Familial metaphysial dysplasia. J. Bone & Joint Surg. *40B*:86, 1958.
Methemoglobinemia.	Scott, E. M. The relation of diaphorase of human erythrocytes to inheritance of methemoglobinemia. J. Clin. Invest. *39*:1176, 1960.
Microcephaly.	Cowie, V. The genetics and sub-classification of microcephaly. J. Ment. Defic. Res. *4*:42, 1960.
Microdontia (generalized).	Steinberg, A. G., J. F. Warren and L. M. Warren. Hereditary generalized microdontia J. Dent. Res. *40*:58–62, 1961.
Microphthalmos.	Gill, E. G. and R. B. Harris. Congenital microphthalmos with cyst formation. Virginia Med. Month. *86*:33, 1959.
Migraine (hemiplegic).	Rosenbaum, H. E. Familial hemiplegic migraine. Neurology *10*:164, 1960.
Möbius syndrome.	Wallis, P. G. Creatinuria in Möbius syndrome. Arch. Dis. Childh. *35*:383, 1960.
Morquio's disease.	Van Noorden, G. K. et al. Ocular findings in Morquio-Ullrich's disease. A.M.A. Arch. Opthal. *64*:585, 1960.
Mucopolysacchariduria.	See *Gargoylism.*
Multiple sclerosis.	Myrianthopoulos, N. C. and R. P. Mackay. Multiple sclerosis in twins and their relatives: Genetic analysis of family histories. Acta genet. et stat. med. (Basel) *10*:33, 1960.
Muscular dystrophy.	Leyburn, P. et al. An investigation of the carrier state in the Duchene type muscular dystrophy. Ann. Hum. Genet. (London) *25*:41–47, 1961.
Myasthenia gravis.	Foldes, F. F. and P. G. McNall. Unusual familial occurrence of myasthenia gravis. J.A.M.A. *174*:418, 1960.
Myoglobinuria.	Kahler, H. J. Die Myoglobinuria. Ergebn. inn. Med. Kinderheilk. *11*:1, 1959.

TRAIT	REFERENCE
Nail-patella syndrome.	Papadimitriou, D. G. Hereditary arthro-osteo-ony-chodysplasia. Southern, Med. J. *53:*186, 1960.
Narcolepsy.	Yoss, R. and D. Daly. Narcolepsy. M. Clin. North America *44:*953, 1960.
Nephritis.	See *Renal dysfunction.*
Nephronophthisis (juvenile).	Ivemark, B. I. et al. Juvenile nephronophthisis. Acta paediat. *49:*480, 1960.
Nephrosis.	Worthen, H. G. et al. Infantile nephrosis. A.M.A.J. Dis. Child. *98:*731, 1959.
Neuritis with brachial predilection.	Jacob, J. C. et al. Heredofamilial neuritis with brachial predilection. Neurology *11:*1025, 1961.
Neurofibromatosis.	Philippart, M. Neurofibromatose hereditaire à large spectre phénotypique. J. génét. hum. (Geneva) *10:* 338–346, 1961.
Neutropenia.	Andrews, J. P. et al. Lethal congenital neutropenia with eosinophilia occurring in two siblings. Am. J. Med. *29:*358, 1960.
Niemann-Pick disease.	Forsythe, W. I. et al. Three cases of Niemann-Pick disease in children. Arch. Dis. Childh. *34:*406, 1959.
Nodal rhythm.	Bacos, J. M. et al. Congenital familial nodal rhythm. Circulation *22:*887, 1960.
Non-spherocytic hemolytic anemia.	Valentine, W. N. et al. A specific erythrocyte gly-colytic enzyme defect (pyruvate kinase) in three subjects with congenital non-spherocytic hemolytic anemia. Tr. A. Am. Physicians *74:*100, 1961.
Ocular albinism.	Gillespie, F. D. Ocular albinism with report of a family with female carriers. Arch. Opthalal. New York *66:*774, 1961.
Odontogenesis imperfecta.	Chaudhry, A. P. et al. Odontogenesis imperfecta. Oral Surg. *14:*1099, 1961.
Ophthalmoplegia.	Lees, F. Congenital, static familial ophthalmoplegia. J. Neurol. Neurosurg. Psychiat. *23:*46, 1960.
Optic atrophy.	See *Leber's optic atrophy.*

TRAIT	REFERENCE
Oral-facial-digital syndrome.	Gorlin, R. J. et al. Hypertrophied frenuli, oligophrenia, familial trembling and anomalies of the hand. New England J. Med. *264:*486, 1961.
Oroticaciduria.	Huguley, C. M., Jr. et al. Refractory megaloblastic anemia associated with excretion of orotic acid. Blood *14:*615, 1959.
Osler-Rendu-Weber syndrome (hemorrhagic telangiectasia).	Hodgson, C. H. et al. Hereditary hemorrhagic telangiectasia and pulmonary arteriovenous fistula. New England J. Med. *261:*625, 1959.
Osteoarthropathy of the fingers.	Allison, A. C. and B. S. Blumberg. Familial osteoarthropathy of the fingers. J. Bone & Joint Surg. *40B:*538, 1958.
Osteochondroses.	Mau, H. Juvenile osteochondroses—enchondral dysostoses. Clin. Orthoped. *11:*154, 1958.
Osteochondritis dissecans.	Stougaard, J. The hereditary factor in osteochondritis dissecans. J. Bone & Joint Surg. *43B:*256, 1961.
Osteogenesis imperfecta.	Smars, G. Osteogenesis imperfecta in Sweden. Svenska Bokforlag. (Stockholm) 1–240, 1961.
Osteo-Onycho-Dysplasia hereditaria (albuminurica).	Schroder, G. Osteo-Onycho-Dysplasia hereditaria. Z. menschl. Vererb. Konstitutionsl. *36:*42–73, 1961.
Osteopoikilosis.	Smith, A. D. and M. Waisman. Connective tissue nevi. Familial occurrence and association with osteopoikilosis. A.M.A. Arch. Dermat. *81:*249, 1960.
Otosclerosis.	Larsson, A. Otosclerosis: a genetic and clinical study. Acta otolaryng. (suppl.) *154:*1, 1960.
Oxaluria.	Hall, E. G. et al. Clinical manifestations of primary hyperoxaluria. Arch. Dis. Childh. *35:*108, 1960.
Pachyonychia congenita.	Witcop, C. J. and R. J. Gorlin. Four hereditary mucosal syndromes. Arch. Dermat. *84:*762, 1961.
Pancreatitis.	Bartholomew, L. G. Newer concepts in pancreatic disease. Gastroenterology *36:*122, 1959.
Parahemophilia.	Didisheim, P. and J. H. Lewis. Congenital disorders of the mechanism for coagulation of blood. Pediatrics *22:*478, 1958.

TRAIT	REFERENCE
Paramyotonia congenita.	LaYoie, W. J. Paramyotonia congenita, clinical features and electromyographic findings. Arch. Phys. Med. *42*:507, 1961.
Parkinsonism-Dementia complex.	Hirano, A. et al. Parkinsonism-dementia complex, an endemic disease on the island of Guam. Brain *84*:642–661, 1961.
Parkinsonism (drug induced).	Myrianthopoulos, N. C., A. A. Kurland and L. T. Kurland. Hereditary predisposition in drug-induced Parkinsonism. Arch. Neurol. *6*:5–9, 1962.
Pelger-Huët anomaly.	Rosse, W. F. and C. W. Gurney. The Pelger-Huët anomaly in three families. Blood *14*:170, 1959.
Pelizaeus-Merzbacher disease.	Tyler, H. R. Pelizaeus-Merzbacher disease. A clinical study. A.M.A. Arch. Neurol. Psychiat. *80*:162, 1958.
Pendred's syndrome (sporadic goiter and congenital deafness).	Fraser, G. R. et al. The syndrome of sporadic goiter and congenital deafness. Quart J. Med. *29*:279, 1960.
Pentosuria (essential).	Khachadurian, A. K. Essential pentosuria. Am. J. Hum. Gen. *14*:249–255, 1962.
Periodic paralysis.	Poskanzer, D. C. and D. N. S. Kerr. A third type of periodic paralysis, with normokalemia and favorable response to sodium chloride. Amer. J. Med. *31*:328, 1961.
Pernicious anemia.	McIntyre, P. A. et al. Genetic factors in predisposition to pernicious anemia. Bull. Johns Hopkins Hosp. *104*:309, 1959.
Peutz-Jeghers syndrome.	See *Intestinal polyposis with mucocutaneous pigmentation.*
Phaeochromocytoma.	Smits, M. and J. Huizinga. Familial occurrence of phaeochromocytoma. Acta. genet. et stat. med. (Basel) *11*:137–153, 1961.
Phenylketonuria.	Carter, C. O. and L. I. Woolf. The birthplaces of parents and grandparents of a series of patients with phenylketonuria in Southeast England. Ann. Hum. Genet. (London) *25*:57, 1961.
Phosphorylase deficiency.	Schmid, R. and R. Mahler. Chronic progressive myopathy with myoglobinuria: Demonstration of a glycogenolytic defect in the muscle. J. Clin. Invest. *38*:2044, 1959.

TRAIT	REFERENCE
Pick's disease (lobar atrophy).	Schenk, V. W. D. Re-examination of a family with Pick's disease. Ann. Hum. Genet. (London) 23:325, 1959.
Pierre-Robin syndrome.	Smith, J. L. and F. R. Stowe. The Pierre-Robin syndrome (glossoptosis, micrognathia, cleft palate). Pediatrics 27:128, 1961.
Poliomyelitis.	Scarabicchi, S. Studio sulla frequenza di casi multipli di poliomielite anteriore acuta nella stessa famiglia. Minerva pediat. 10:556, 1958.
Polycystic kidney.	Lundin, P. M. and I. Olow. Polycystic kidneys in newborns, infants and children. A clinical and pathological study. Acta paediat. (Uppsala) 50:185, 1961.
Polycystic liver and kidney.	Lathrop, D. B. Cystic disease of the liver and kidney. Pediatrics 24:215, 1959.
Polycythemia.	Nixon, R. K. et al. Nephrogenic polycythemia. A.M.A. Arch. Intern. Med. 106:797, 1960.
Polydactyly.	Walker, J. T. A pedigree of extra-digit-V polydactyly in a Batutsi family. Ann. Hum. Genet. (London) 25:65, 1961.
Popliteal webbing.	Champion, R. and J. C. F. Cregan. Congenital popliteal webbing in siblings. J. Bone & Joint Surg. 41B:355, 1959.
Porphyria.	Eales, L. The porphyrins and the porphyrias. Ann. Rev. Med. 12:251, 1961.
Pre-eclampsia.	Adams, E. M. and A. Finlayson. Familial aspects of pre-eclampsia and hypertension in pregnancy. Lancet ii: 1375–1378, 1961.
Progeria.	Gabr, M. et al. Progeria, a pathologic study. J. Pediat. 57:70, 1960.
Progressive muscular atrophy.	Brown, M. R. The inheritance of progressive muscular atrophy as a dominant trait in two New England families. New England J. Med. 262:1280, 1960.
Pseudocholinesterase deficiency.	Harris, H. et al. The pseudocholinesterase variants, etc. Acta genet. et stat. med. (Basel) 10:1, 1960.
Pseudoxanthoma elasticum.	Berlyne, G. M. et al. The genetics of pseudodoxanthoma elasticum. Quart. J. Med. 30:201, 1961.

TRAIT	REFERENCE
Psoriasis.	Ward, J. H. and F. E. Stephens. Inheritance of psoriasis in a Utah kindred. Arch. Dermat. *84*:589, 1961.
Radial heads (dislocation).	Cockshott, W. P. and A. Omololu. Familial congenital posterior dislocation of both radial heads. J. Bone & Joint Surg. *40B*:483, 1958.
Refsum's disease.	Jager, B. V. et al. Occurrence of retinal pigmentation, ophthalmoplegia, ataxia, deafness and heart block. Am. J. Med. *29*:888, 1960.
Renal agensis.	Carpentier, P. J. and E. L. Potter. Nuclear sex and genital malformation in 48 cases of renal agensis, etc. Am. J. Obstet. Gynec. 78:235, 1959.
Renal dysfunction with associated nerve deafness (Alport's syndrome).	Cohen, M. M., G. Cassady and B. L. Hanna. A genetic study of hereditary renal dysfunction with associated nerve deafness. Am. J. Hum. Genet. *13:* 379–389, 1961.
Renal glycosuria.	Gjone, E. Idiopathic renal glycosuria in three generations with high incidence. Nord. Med. *59*:306, 1958.
Renal stone.	McGeown, M. G. Heredity in renal stone disease. Clin. Sci. *19*:465, 1960.
Renal tubular acidosis.	Huth, E. J. et al. The renal excretion of hydrogen ion in renal tubular acidosis, etc. Am. J. Med. *29:* 586, 1960.
Retinal aplasia.	Sorsby, A. and C. E. Williams. Retinal aplasia as a clinical entity. Brit. Med. J. *1*:293, 1960.
Retinitis pigmentosa combined with congenital deafness.	Hallgren, B. Retinitis pigmentosa combined with congenital deafness; with vestibulo-cerebellar ataxia and mental abnormality in a proportion of cases. Acta psychiat. neurol. scand. (suppl.) 138, *34*:1–101, 1959.
Retinoblastoma.	Manchester, P. T. Jr. Retinoblastoma among offspring of adult survivors. A. M. A. Arch. Ophthal. *65*:546–549, 1961.
Retinoschisis.	Gieser, E. P. and H. F. Falls. Hereditary retinoschisis. Am. J. Ophthal. *51*:1193–1200, 1961.
Rhabdomyolysis.	Farmer, T. A. Jr. et al. Idiopathic recurrent rhab-

TRAIT   REFERENCE

domyolysis associated with myoglobininuria. New England J. Med. *264*:60, 1961.

Scaphocephaly.   Bell, H. S. et al. Familial scaphocephaly. J. Neurosurg. *18*:239, 1961.

Scimitar syndrome.   Neill, C. A. et al. The familial occurrence of hypoplastic right lung with systemic arterial supply and venous drainage, "Scimitar syndrome." Bull. Johns Hopkins Hosp. *107*:1, 1960.

Seitelberger's amaurotic idiocy.   Nakai, H. et al. Seitelberger's spastic amaurotic axonal idiocy. Pediatrics *25*:441, 1960.

Sensory radicular neuropathy.   Pallis, C. and J. Schneeweiss. Hereditary sensory radicular neuropathy. Am. J. Med. *32*:110, 1962.

Sex-linked deaf-mutism associated with albinism.   Margolis, E. A new hereditary syndrome—sex-linked deaf mutism associated with total albinism. Acta genet. et stat. med. (Basel) *12*:12–19, 1962.

Sickle cell anemia.   Rossi, E. The abnormal hemoglobins. Am. J. Med. Sci. *240*:93, 1960.

Sjögren's syndrome.   Denko, C. W. and D. M. Bergenstal. The Sicca syndrome (Sjögren's syndrome). Arch. Intern. Med. *105*:849, 1960.

Sjögren-Larsson syndrome (ichthyosis, spastic diplegia and mental deficiency).   Richards, B. W. Congenital ichthyosis, spastic diplegia and mental deficiency. Brit. Med. J. *2*:714, 1960.

Spastic quadriplegia.   Blumel, J. et al. Spastic quadriplegia combined with congenital ichthyosiform erythroderma and oligophrenia. A.M.A.J. Dis. Child. *96*:724, 1958.

Spherocytosis.   Morton, N. E. et al. Genetics of spherocytosis. Am. J. Hum. Genet. *14*:170–184, 1962.

Spinocerebellar ataxia.   Jampel, R. S. et al. Ophthalmoplagia and retinal degeneration associated with spinocerebellar ataxia. Arch. Ophthal. (New York) *66*:247, 1961.

Steatocystoma multiplex.   Vineyard, W. R. and R. A. Scott. Steatocystoma multiplex with pachyonychia congenita. Arch. Dermat. *84*:824, 1961.

Strümpell-Lorrain's spasmodic paraplegia.   Hariga, J. and E. Matthys. De la paraplégie spasmodique de Strümpell-Lorrain à l'amyotrophie de Charcot-Marie-Tooth. J. génét. hum. (Geneva) *10*: 326–337, 1961.

TRAIT	REFERENCE
Sturge-Weber's disease.	Patau, K. et al. Partial trisomy syndromes. I. Sturge-Weber's disease. Am. J. Hum. Genet. *13:* 287, 1961.
Tangier disease.	Fredrickson, D. S. Tangier disease. Ann. Intern. Med. 55:1016, 1961.
Tapeto-retinal degeneration (central).	Barkman, Y. A clinical study of a central tapeto-retinal degeneration. Acta Ophthal. *39:*663–670, 1961.
Tapeto-retinal degeneration (peripheral).	Ammann, F., D. Klein and H. R. Böhringer. Resultats préliminaires d'une enquête sur la frequence et la distribution géographique des dégénérescences tapétorétiniennes en suisse. J. génét. hum. (Geneva) *10:*99–127, 1961.
Tay-Sachs disease.	See *Amaurotic idiocy.*
Teeth.	Witcop, C. J. Dental genetics 1959. J. Am. Dent. A *60:*564, 1960.
Telangiectasia.	Ecker, J. A. et al. Gastrointestinal bleeding in hereditary hemorrhagic telangiectasia. Am. J. Gastroent. *33:*411, 1960.
Testicular feminization.	Chu, E. H. Y. et al. Karyotypic analysis of a male pseudohermaphrodite with the syndrome of feminizing testes. J. Clin. Endocrinol. *20:*1608, 1960.
Thalassemia.	Bannerman, R. M. Thalassemia. A Survey of Some Aspects. New York, Grune & Stratton, Inc., 1961.
Thrombocytopenic purpura.	Jones, T. G. et al. Maternal and neonatal platelet antibodies in a case of congenital thrombocytopenia. Lancet *ii:*1008, 1961.
Torticollis.	Gedda, L. et al. Nuove osservazioni di torcicollo osseo in gemelli MZ e in fratelli mononati. Acta genet. med. gemell. 7:133, 1958.
Treacher Collin's syndrome.	See *Franceschetti's syndrome.*
Tremor.	Larsson, T. and T. Sjögren. Essential tremor. Acta psychiat. neurol. scand. *36:*1–176. Suppl. 144, 1960.
Tuberous sclerosis.	Hudolin, V. La sclerose tubereuse. J. génét. hum. (Geneva) *10:*128–155, 1961.
Tubular absorption defect.	Sheldon, W. et al. A familial tubular absorption

TRAIT	REFERENCE
	defect of glucose and amino acids. Arch. Dis. Childh. *36*:90, 1961.
Turner's syndrome.	Boyer, S. H. et al. The lack of influence of parental age and birth order in the aetiology of nuclear sex chromatin-negative Turner's syndrome. Ann. Hum. Genet. (London) *25*:69, 1961.
Undritz anomaly (hypersegmentation of the nuclei of the polymorphonuclear leukocytes).	Undritz, E. Eine neue Sippe mit erblich konstitutioneller Hochsegmentierung der Neutrophilenkerne. Schweiz. Med. Wschr. *88*:1000, 1958.
von Gierke's disease.	Hsia, D. Y-Y. and E. G. Kot. Detection of heterozygous carriers in glycogen storage disease of the liver (von Gierke's disease). Nature (London) *183*:1331, 1959.
von Hippel-Lindau syndrome.	Schechterman, L. Lindau's disease. Report of an unusual case and two additional cases in a Negro family. Med. Ann. District of Columbia *30*:64, 1961.
von Recklinghausen's disease.	See *Neurofibromatosis.*
von Willebrand's disease.	Pitney, W. R. and B. J. Arnold. Laboratory findings in families of patients suffering from von Willebrand's disease. Brit. J. Haemat. *6*:81, 1960.
Waardenburg-Klein syndrome.	Lavergne, G. Probleme d'eugenisme pose par une famille atteinte du syndrome de Waardenburg-Klein. J. génét. hum. (Geneva) *10*:80–85, 1961.
Werner's syndrome.	Motulsky, A. G. et al. Werner's syndrome: Chromosomes, genes and the ageing process. Lancet *i*:160, 1962.
Whipple's disease.	Gross, J. B. et al. Whipple's disease. Gastroenterology *36*:65, 1959.
White forelock.	Loewenthal, L. J. A. Albinoidism with epitheliomatosis. Brit. J. Dermat. *71*:37, 1959.
Wilms' tumor.	Ström, T. A Wilms' tumor family. Acta paediat. *46*:601, 1957.
Wilson's disease.	Walshe, J. M. and J. N. Cumings. Wilson's disease. Some current concepts. Blackwell Scientific Publications, Oxford. 1–292, 1961.

TRAIT	REFERENCE
Wolff-Parkinson-White syndrome.	Schiebler, G. L. et al. Familial cardiomegaly in association with the Wolff-Parkinson-White Syndrome. Am. Heart J. *58:*113, 1959.
Xanthomatosis.	Wolman, M. et al. Primary familial xanthomatosis with involvement and calcification of the adrenals. Pediatrics *28:*742, 1961.
Xeroderma pigmentosum.	Giller, H. and W. C. Kaufmann. Ocular lesions in xeroderma pigmentosum. A.M.A. Arch. Ophthal. *62:*130, 1959.
Zollinger-Ellison syndrome.	Schmid, J. R. et al. Relationship of multiple endocrine adenomas to the syndrome of ulcerogenic islet cell adenomas (Zollinger-Ellison). Am. J. Med. *264:*223, 1961.

GENERAL
LITERATURE
CITED

Aird, I., H. H. Bentall, and J. A. F. Roberts. 1953. A relationship between cancer of the stomach and the ABO blood groups. Brit. Med. J. *1*:799–801.

Allison, A. C. 1955. Aspects of polymorphism in man. Cold Spring Harbor Symp. Quant. Biol. *20*:239–255.

Anderson, R. C. 1954. Causative factors underlying congenital heart malformations. I. Patent ductus arteriosus. Pediatrics *14*:143–152.

Anderson, V. E., H. O. Goodman, and S. C. Reed. 1958. Variables Related to Human Breast Cancer. University of Minnesota Press, Minneapolis.

Aronson, S. M., and B. W. Volk. 1962. Chap. 27 in The Cerebral Sphingolipidoses. Academic Press, New York.

Assum, H. W. 1936. Untersuchungen über die Erblichkeit des angeborenen Klump-fussleidens. Ztschr. f. Orthop. *65*:1–42.

Beckman, L., J. A. Böök, and E. Lander. 1960. Anthropological traits in paternity tests. Hereditas *46*:543–569.

Bender, M. A., and Sheldon Wolff. 1961. X-ray induced chromosome aberrations and reproductive death in mammalian cells. Am. Nat. 95:39–52.

Bertinshaw, D., S. D. Lawler, H. A. Holt, B. H. Kirman, and R. R. Race. 1950. The combination of blood groups in a sample of 475 people in a London hospital. Ann. Eugenics 15:234–242.

Blair, P. B. 1960. A mutation in the mouse mammary tumor virus. Cancer Res. 20:635.

Bond, T. P., W. C. Levin, D. R. Celander, and W. M. Guest. 1962. "Mild hemophilia" affecting both males and females. N. E. Jour. Med. 266:220–223.

Böök, J. A. 1948. A contribution to the genetics of congenital clubfoot. Hereditas 34:289–300.

Böök, J. A. 1953. A genetic and neuropsychiatric investigation of a North Swedish population. Acta Genetica et Statistica Medica 4:1–100; 133–139; 345–414.

Böök, J. A. 1953. Oligophrenia. Chap. 17 in Sorsby's Clinical Genetics. C. V. Mosby Co., St. Louis.

Böök, J. A., and S. Rayner. 1950. A clinical and genetical study of anencephaly. Am. J. Hum. Genet. 2:61–84.

Böök, J. A., and S. C. Reed. 1950. Empiric risk figures in mongolism. J.A.M.A. 143:730–732.

Böök, J. A., B. Santesson, and P. Zetterqvist. 1961. Association between congenital heart malformation and chromosomal variations. Acta Pediatrica 50:217–227.

Bowen, R. 1953. Allergy in identical twins. J. Allergy 24:234–244.

Bulmer, M. G. 1960. The familial incidence of twinning. Ann. Hum. Genet. 24:1–3.

Carter, C., and D. MacCarthy. 1951. Incidence of mongolism and its diagnosis in the newborn. Brit. J. Soc. Med. 5:83–90.

Carter, C. O. 1961. Inheritance of congenital pyloric stenosis. Brit. Med. Bull. 17:251–254.

Carter, C. O., and K. A. Evans. 1961. Risk of parents who have had one child with Down's syndrome (mongolism) having another child similarly affected. Lancet ii:785–788.

Carter, C. O., J. L. Hamerton, P. E. Polani, A. Gunalp, and S. D. V. Weller. 1960. Chromosomal translocations as a cause of familial mongolism. Lancet *ii*, 678–680.

Chung, C. S., and N. E. Morton. 1961. Selection at the ABO locus. Am. J. Hum. Genet. *13*:9–27.

Clarke, C. A. 1961. Blood groups and disease. Prog. Med. Genetics *1*:81–119.

Clarke, C. A. 1962. Genetics for the Clinician. F. A. Davis Co., Philadelphia.

Clarke, C. M., J. H. Edwards, and V. Smallpiece. 1961. 21-trisomy/normal mosaicism in an intelligent child with some mongoloid characters. Lancet *i*:1028–1030.

Conrad, C. 1940. Die erbliche Fallsucht. Vol. 3, Part 2 of A. Guetts' Handbuch der Erbkrankheiten. G. Thieme, Leipzig.

Cruz-Coke, R. 1959. The hereditary factor in hypertension. Acta Genetica et Statistica Medica *9*:207–212.

Davenport, C. B. 1923. Body build and its inheritance. Carnegie Institute of Washington Publication No. 329.

Eaton, J. W., and R. J. Weil. 1953. The mental health of the Hutterites. Scient. Am. *189*:31–37.

Edwards, J. H. 1958. Congenital malformations of the central nervous system in Scotland. Brit. J. Prev. Soc. Med. *12*:115–130.

Edwards, J. H. 1960. The simulation of mendelism. Acta Genetica et Statistica Medica *10*:63–70.

Edwards, J. H. 1961. Seasonal incidence of congenital disease in Birmingham. Ann. Hum. Genet. (Lond.) *25*:89–93.

Edwards, J. H. 1961. The syndrome of sex-linked hydrocephalus. Arch. Dis. Child. *36*:481–493.

Edwards, J. H., D. G. Harnden, A. H. Cameron, V. M. Crosse, and O. H. Wolff. 1960. A new trisomic syndrome. Lancet *i*:787–789.

Faber, A. 1937. Erbbiologische untersuchungen über die Anlage zur "angeborenen" Hüftverrenkung. Zeit f. Orthop. *66*:140–166.

Farris, E. J., and M. Garrison. 1954. Emotional impact of successful donor insemination. Obs. & Gyn. 3(1):19–20.

Forssman, H., and O. Lehmann. 1962. Chromosome studies in eleven families with mongolism in more than one member. Acta Paediatrica 51:180–188.

Fraser, F. C. 1959. Antenatal factors in congenital defects. N. Y. State Jour. Med. 59:1597–1605.

Freire-Maia, N. 1960. Deleterious mutations in man. Eug. Quart. 7:193–203.

Fujiki, N., A. L. Drew, M. Miyake, H. Nemoto, C. Sujaku, and T. Shimada. 1961. A case of phenylketonuria in the Eta resulting from the mating of a homozygous father and heterozygous mother. Am. J. Hum. Gen. 13:64–68.

Gauld, R. L., and Read, F. E. M. 1940. Studies of rheumatic disease. Age at onset of primary rheumatic attack. J. Clin. Invest. 19:729–734.

Gedda, L. 1961. Twins in history and science. Charles C Thomas, Springfield, Ill.

Gibson, L. E., and R. E. Cooke. 1959. A test for concentration of electrolytes in sweat in cystic fibrosis of the pancreas utilizing pilocarpine by iontophoresis. Pediatrics 23:545–549.

Good, R. A., W. D. Kelly, J. Rötstein, and R. L. Varco. 1962. Immunological Deficiency Diseases. Progress in Allergy, vol. 6.

Graham, D. C. 1960. Leukemia following x-ray therapy for ankylosing spondylitis. A.M.A. Arch. Int. Med. 105:51–59.

Gray, F. G., R. W. Quinn, and J. P. Quinn. 1952. A long term survey of rheumatic and non-rheumatic families. Am. J. Med. 13:400–412.

Greenberg, M., O. Pellitteri, and J. Barton. 1957. Frequency of defects in infants whose mothers had rubella during pregnancy. J.A.M.A. 165:675–678.

Gregg, N. M. 1941. Congenital cataract following German measles in mother. Tran. Ophth. Soc. Australia 3:35–46.

Grunnet, J. 1957. Heredity in diabetes mellitus. Opera ex Domo Biolog. Hered. Human. 39:1–128.

Guthrie, R. 1961. Blood screening for phenylketonuria. J.A.M.A. 178:863.

Hall, E. M., and L. A. Anderson. 1943. The incidence of rheumatic stigmas in hearts which are usually considered nonrheumatic. Am. Heart. J. 25:64–80.

Hamerton, J. L., V. Cowie, F. Giannelli, S. Briggs, and P. E. Polani. 1961. Differential transmission of Down's syndrome (mongolism) through male and female translocation carriers. Lancet *ii*:956–958.

Harnden, D. G., and P. A. Jacobs. 1961. Cytogenetics of abnormal sexual development in man. Brit. Med. Bull. *17*:206–212.

Hart, V. L. 1947. Congenital dislocation and congenital subluxation of the hip. Minn. Med. *30*:889–896.

Heston, W. E., and G. Vlahakis. 1961. Elimination of the effect of the A^y gene on pulmonary tumors in mice by alteration of its effect on normal growth. J. Nat. Cancer Inst. *27*:1189–1196.

Hollingshead, A. B., and F. C. Redlich. 1958. Social Class and Mental Illness: A Community Study. John Wiley & Sons. New York.

Hsia, D. Y-Y. 1959. Inborn Errors of Metabolism. The Year Book Publishers. Chicago.

Idelberger, K. 1951. Die erbpathologie der sogenannten angeborenen Huftverrenkung. Urban and Schwarzenberg. Munich.

Ingram, V. M. 1961. Hemoglobin and Its Abnormalities. Charles C Thomas. Springfield, Ill.

Jackson, W. P. U. 1955. A concept of diabetes. Lancet *ii*:626–631.

Jacobs, P. A., and Strong, J. A. 1959. A case of human intersexuality having a possible XXY sex-determining mechanism. Nature *183*:302.

Johnston, A. W., and V. A. McKusick, 1962. A sex-linked recessive form of spastic paraplegia. Am. J. Hum. Gen. *14*:83–94.

Kallman, F. J. 1946. The genetic theory of schizophrenia. Am. J. Psychiat. *103*:309–322.

Kallman, F. J. 1948. Heredity and constitution in relation to the treatment of mental disorders. In P. H. Hoch: Failures in Psychiatric Treatment. Grune & Stratton, New York.

Kallman, F. J. 1953. Heredity in Health and Mental Disorder. W. W. Norton & Co., New York.

Kallman, F. J., and D. Reisner. 1943. Twin studies on genetic variations in resistance to tuberculosis. J. Hered. *34*:269–276, 293–301.

Kallman, F. J., and G. Sander. 1947. The genetics of epilepsy. In P. H. Hoch and R. P. Knight (editors). Epilepsy. Grune & Stratton, New York.

Kalmus, H. 1955. The discrimination by the nose of the dog of individual human odours and in particular of the odours of twins. British Journal of Animal Behaviour. 3(1):25–31.

Kaplan, I. I. 1958. The treatment of female sterility with x-ray therapy directed to the pituitary and ovaries. Am. J. Obst. & Gynec. 76:447–453.

Karlish, A. J., and A. L. Tarnoky. 1960. Mucoviscidosis as a factor in chronic lung disease in adults. Lancet ii:514–515.

Keith, H. M., and R. P. Gage. 1960. Neurological lesions in relation to asphyxia of the newborn and factors of pregnancy: long term follow-up. Pediatrics 26: 616–622.

Keys, A., O. Mickelsen, E. V. O. Miller, and C. B. Chapman. 1950. The relation in man between cholesterol levels in the diet and in the blood. Science 112: 79–81.

Kimball, O. P., and A. H. Hersh. 1955. The genetics of epilepsy. Acta Genet. Med. et Gemell. 4:131–142.

Kobayasi, Y. 1958. A genetic study on harelip and cleft palate. Jap. J. Hum. Genet. 3:73–107.

Krivit, W., and R. A. Good. 1956. The simultaneous occurrence of leukemia and mongolism. A.M.A. J. Dis. Child. 91:218–222.

Landsteiner, K., and A. S. Wiener. 1940. An agglutinable factor in human blood recognized by immune sera for rhesus blood. Proc. Soc, Exp. Biol. 43:223.

Lejeune, J., Gautier, M., and Turpin, R. 1959. Les chromosomes humains en culture de tissus. C. R. Acad. Sci., Paris 248:1721.

Lennox, W. G. 1951. The heredity of epilepsy as told by relatives and twins. J.A.M.A. 146:529–536.

Levine, P. 1958. The influence of the ABO system on Rh hemolytic disease. Human Biology 30:14–28.

Lundström, R. 1962. Rubella during pregnancy. Acta Paediatrica 51 (Suppl. 133).

Lurie, M. B., P. Zappasodi, A. M. Dannenberg, Jr., and G. H. Weiss. 1952. On the mechanism of genetic resistance to tuberculosis and its mode of inheritance. Am. J. Hum. Genet. 4:302–314.

MacMahon, B., and T. McKeown. 1955. Infantile hypertrophic pyloric stenosis: data on 81 pairs of twins. Acta Genet. Med. et Gemell. *4*:320–329.

MacMahon, B., T. McKeown, and R. G. Record. 1953. The incidence and life expectation of children with congenital heart disease. Brit. Heart J. *15*:121–129.

MacMahon, B., T. F. Pugh, and T. H. Ingalls. 1953. Anencephalus, spina bifida and hydrocephalus. Brit. J. Prev. Soc. Med. 7:211–219.

Masland, R. L., S. B. Sarason, and T. Gladwin. 1958. Mental Subnormality. Biological, Psychological and Cultural Factors. Basic Books, New York.

Matsunaga, E. 1955. Intra-uterine selection by the ABO incompatibility of mother and foetus. Am. J. Hum. Genet. 7:66–71.

McDermott, W., K. Deuschle, J. Adair, H. Fulmer, and B. Loughlin. 1960. Introducing modern medicine in a Navajo community. Science *131*:280–287.

McKeown, T., B. MacMahon, and C. G. Parsons. 1953. The familial incidence of congenital malformation of the heart. Brit. Heart J. *15*:273–277.

McKeown, T., B. MacMahon, and R. G. Record. 1952. Evidence of postnatal environmental influence in the etiology of infantile pyloric stenosis. Arch. Dis. Child. *27*:386–390.

Meier, H., and G. Yerganian. 1961. Spontaneous diabetes mellitus in the Chinese hamster. Diabetes *10*:12–18.

Merrell, D. J. 1951. Inheritance of manic-depressive psychosis. Arch. Neurol. & Psychiat. *66*:272–279.

Metrakos, J. D., K. Metrakos, and H. Baxter. 1958. Clefts of the lip and palate in twins, including a discordant pair whose monozygosity was confirmed by skin transplants. Plast. Reconst. Surg. *22*(2):109–122.

Metrakos, K., and J. D. Metrakos. 1961. Genetics of convulsive disorders. II. Genetic and electroencephalographic studies in centrencephalic epilepsy. Neurology *11*:474–483.

Miller, O. J., W. R. Breg, R. D. Smickel, and W. Tretter. 1961. A family with an XXXXY male, a leukaemic male and two 21-trisomic females. Lancet *ii*: (7193):78–79.

Moorhead, P. S., W. J. Mellman, and C. Wenar. 1961. A familial chromosome translocation associated with speech and mental retardation. Am. J. Hum. Genet. *13*:32–46.

Morton, N. E. 1960. The mutational load due to detrimental genes in man. Am. J. Hum. Genet. *12*:348–364.

Muller, H. J. 1950. Our load of mutations. Am. J. Hum. Genet. *2*:111–176.

Müller, W. M. 1926. Zur Aetiologie des angeborenen Klumpfusses unter besonderer Berücksichtigung seiner Vererburg. Arch. d. Julius Klaus-Stift. f. Vererbgsforsch. *2*:1–37.

Murphy, D. P. 1947. Congenital Malformations. J. B. Lippincott Company, Philadelphia.

Neel, J. V. 1953. The detection of the genetic carriers of inherited disease. Chap. 3 in Sorsby's Clinical Genetics. C. V. Mosby Co., St. Louis.

Neel, J. V., W. J. Schull, et al. 1956. The Effect of Exposure to the Atomic Bombs on Pregnancy Termination in Hiroshima and Nagasaki. Publ. No. 461. National Research Council. Washington 25, D. C.

Öster, J. 1953. Mongolism. Opera ex Domo Biolog. Hered. Human. *32*:1–206.

Oxorn, H. 1959. Rubella and pregnancy: a study of 47 cases. Am. J. Obst. & Gynec. *77*:628–31.

Parnell, R. W. 1958. Behavior and Physique. Edward Arnold, London.

Penrose, L. S. 1946. Familial data on 144 cases of anencephaly, spina bifida and congenital hydrocephaly. Ann. Eugen. *13*:73–98.

Penrose, L. S. 1957. Genetics of anencephaly. J. Ment. Defic. Res. *1*:4.

Phair, G. M. 1947. The Wisconsin cleft palate program. J. Speech Disorders *12*: 410–414.

Pincus, G., and P. White. 1933. On the inheritance of diabetes mellitus. I. Am. J. Med. Sci. *186*:1–14.

Pincus, G., and P. White. 1934. On the inheritance of diabetes mellitus. II. Am. J. Med. Sci. *188*:159–168; 782–790.

Polani, P. E., and M. Campbell. 1960. Factors in the causation of persistent ductus arteriosus. Ann. Hum. Genet. *24*:343–357.

Price, B. 1950. Primary biases in twin studies. Am. J. Hum. Genet. *2*:293–352.

Race, R. R., and R. Sanger. 1962. Blood Groups in Man. Fourth Edition. Charles C Thomas. Springfield, Ill.

Record, R. G. 1961. Anencephalus in Scotland. Brit. J. Prev. Soc. Med. 15:93–105.

Record, R. G., and J. H. Edwards. 1958. Environmental influences related to the aetiology of congenital dislocation of the hip. Brit. J. Prev. Soc. Med. 12:8–22.

Record, R. G., and T. McKeown. 1949. Congenital malformations of the central nervous system. I. Brit. J. Prev. Soc. Med. 3:183–219.

Record, R. G., and T. McKeown. 1950a. Congenital malformations of the central nervous system. II. Brit. J. Prev. Soc. Med. 4:26–50.

Record, R. G., and T. McKeown. 1950b. Congenital malformations of the central nervous system. III. Brit. J. Prev. Soc. Med. 4:217–220.

Reed, S. C. 1936. Harelip in the house mouse. Genetics 21:339–374.

Reed, S. C. 1961. Counseling in medical genetics. *DeGenetica Medica* Pars Tertia. Edizioni Instituto Mendel., pp. 152–177.

Reed, S. C., and E. B. Nordlie. 1961. Genetic counseling: for children of mixed racial ancestry. Eug. Quart. 8:157–163.

Reed, S. C., E. W. Reed, and J. D. Palm. 1954. Fertility and intelligence among families of the mentally deficient. Eug. Quart. 1:44–52.

Reepmaker, J., L. E. Nijenhuis, and J. J. VanLoghem. 1962. The inhibiting effect of ABO incompatibility on rh immunization in pregnancy: a statistical analysis of 1,742 families. Am. J. Hum. Genet. 14:185–198.

Rintoul, J. R., and N. F. Kirkman. 1961. The myenteric plexus in infantile hypertrophic pyloric stenosis. Arch. Dis. Child. 36:474–480.

Roberts, J. A. F. 1962. Methodology in Human Genetics. Ed. W. J. Burdette. Holden-Day Inc., San Francisco.

Rosenthal, D. 1959. Some factors associated with concordance and discordance with respect to schizophrenia in monozygotic twins. J. Nerv. & Ment. Dis. 129:1–10.

Rosenthal, D. 1961. Sex distribution and the severity of illness among samples of schizophrenic twins. J. Psychiat. Res. 1:26–36.

Rowley, J. D. 1962. A review of recent studies of chromosomes in mongolism. Am. J. Ment. Def. 66:529–532.

Rutherford, R. N., and A. L. Banks. 1954. Semi-adoption techniques and results. Fertil. Steril. 5:271–281.

Schachter, F. F., and V. Apgar. 1959. Perinatal asphyxia and psychologic signs of brain damage in childhood. Pediatrics 24:1016–1025.

Schwartz, H. A., and P. Levine. 1943. Studies on the Rh factor. Am. J. Obst. & Gynec. 46:827–835.

Schwartz, M. 1953. Allergy. Chap. 28 in Sorsby's Clinical Genetics. C. V. Mosby, St. Louis.

Sheldon, W. H. 1954. Atlas of Men. Harper & Brothers. New York.

Shields, J. 1958. Twins brought up apart. Eugen. Rev. 50:115–123.

Shwachman, H., and L. L. Kulczycki. 1958. Long term study of one hundred five patients with cystic fibrosis. Am. J. Dis. Child. 96:6–15.

Skodak, M., and H. M. Skeels. 1949. A final follow-up study of one hundred adopted children. J. Genet. Psychol. 75:85–125.

Smoller, M., and D. Y. Y. Hsia. 1959. Studies on the genetic mechanisms of cystic fibrosis of the pancreas. Am. J. Dis. Child. 98:277–292.

Spaich, D., and M. Ostertag. 1936. Untersuchungen über allergische Erkrankugen bei Zwillingen. Zeit. f. mensch. Vererb.-u Konstitutionslehre 19:731.

Stearns, P. E., K. E. Droulard, and F. H. Sahler. 1960. Studies bearing on fertility of male and female mongoloids. Am. J. Ment. Def. 65:37–41.

Steinberg, A. G. 1959. The genetics of diabetes: a review. Ann. N. Y. Acad. Sci. 82:197–207.

Steinberg, A. G., and D. C. Brown. 1960. On the incidence of cystic fibrosis of the pancreas. Am. J. Hum. Genet. 12:416–424.

Stenstedt, A. 1952. A study in manic depressive psychosis; clinical, social and genetic investigation. Acta psychiat. et neurol. scandinav. (Supp. 79) pp. 1–111.

Stern, C. 1953. Model estimates of the frequency of white and near-white segregants in the American Negro. Acta Genetica et Statistica Medica 4:281–298.

Stern, C. 1960. Principles of Human Genetics. W. H. Freeman and Company, San Francisco.

Stevenson, A. C., and E. A. Cheeseman. 1956. Heredity and rheumatic fever. Some later information about data collected in 1950–51. Ann. Hum. Genet. *21:* 139–144.

Stewart, A., J. Webb, and D. Hewitt. 1958. A survey of childhood malignancies. Brit. Med. J. *i:*1495–1508.

Stewart, S. F. 1951. Clubfoot: its incidence, cause and treatment. J. Bone & Joint Surg. *33*–A:577–590.

Sutow, W. W., and A. W. Pryde. 1956. Incidence of spina bifida occulta in relation to age. A.M.A. J. Dis. Child. *91:*211–217.

Test, A. R., and H. F. Falls. 1947. Dominant inheritance of cleft lip and palate in five generations. J. Oral Surg. *5:*292–297.

Therman, E., K. Patau, D. W. Smith, and R. I. DeMars. 1961. The D trisomy syndrome and XO gonadal dysgenesis in two sisters. Am. J. Hum. Genet. *13:* 193–204.

Thomas, Caroline. 1959. Familial patterns in hypertension and coronary heart disease. Circulation *20:*25–29 (July).

Thompson, M. W. 1961. Reproduction in two female mongols. Canad. J. Genet. Cytol. *3:*351–354.

Tough, I. M., A. G. Baikie, D. G. Harnden, M. J. King, W. M. Court-Brown, K. E. Buckton, P. A. Jacobs, and J. A. McBride 1961. Cytogenetic studies in chronic myeloid leukaemia and acute leukaemia associated with mongolism. Lancet *i:*411–417.

Tough, I. M., K. E. Buckton, A. G. Baikie, and W. M. Court-Brown. 1960. X-ray-induced chromosome damage in man. Lancet *ii:*849–851.

Transler, D. G. 1960. Influence of uterine site on occurrence of spontaneous cleft lip in mice. Science *132:*420–421.

Uchida, I. A. 1953. Possible genetic factors in the etiology of rheumatic fever. Am. J. Hum. Genet. *5:*61–69.

Van Arsdel, P. P., Jr., and A. G. Motulsky. 1959. Frequency and heritability of asthma and allergic rhinitis in college students. Acta Genetica et Statistica Medica *9:*101–114.

Wallace, B., and Th. Dobzhansky. 1959. Radiation, Genes and Man. Henry Holt and Company. New York.

Wang, H. L., N. E. Morton, and H. A. Waisman. 1961. Increased reliability for the determination of the carrier state in phenylketonuria. Am. J. Hum. Genet. 13:255–261.

Warburton, D., and F. C. Fraser. 1959. Genetic aspects of abortion. Clin. Obs. Gyn. 2:22–35.

Warkany, J. 1953. Disturbance of embryonic development by maternal vitamin deficiences. J. Cell. & Comp. Physiol. 43(Supp. 1):207–236.

Warkany, J., R. C. Nelson, and E. Schraffenberger. 1943. Congenital malformations induced in rats by maternal malnutritional deficiency. Am. J. Dis. Child. 65:882.

Wilson, M. G., and M. Schweitzer. 1954. Pattern of hereditary susceptibility in rheumatic fever. Circulation 10:699–704.

Wolanski, N. 1961. A new graphic method for the evaluation of the tempo and harmony of physical growth of children. Hum. Biol. 33:283–292.

Woolf, C. M. 1955. Investigations on genetic aspects of carcinoma of the stomach and breast. University of California Publications in Public Health 2:265–350.

Woolf, L. I., R. Griffiths, A. Moncrieff, S. Coates, and F. Dillistone. 1958. The dietary treatment of phenylketonuria. Arch. Dis. Child. 33:31–45.

INDEX

Page numbers in *italics* refer to tables.

A-B-O system, of blood groups, 137
    effect on likelihood of erythro-
        blastosis in infant, 143
abortion(s), in anencephaly, spina bif-
    ida, and hydrocephaly, *76*
    in diabetes mellitus, 91
acetabular dysplasia. See *hip, congenital
    dislocation of.*
achondroplastic dwarfism, illustrative ex-
    ample, 170
acromicria, congenital. See *Down's syn-
    drome.*
adoption, categories of children most
    often available for, 159
    of children of mentally retarded par-
        ents, 66
    of mixed racial ancestry, 159
    scarcity of children available for, 65
agammaglobulinemia, 144
age, of mother, as factor in incidence of
    Down's syndrome, 51, *51*
agglutination, blood, 137
albinism, application of laws of genetics
    to, 17
    carried by heterozygote, 29

albinism, illustrative case, 32
allergies, 132–136
    counseling problems in, 134
    genetic background of, 133
    hereditary nature of, 132
    illustrative example, 136
    incidence of, 133
    multiple, 134
    risk of incidence of, 134
    twin studies in, 132, *133*
anemia, sickle cell, and malaria, 218
    detection of carriers, 32
anencephaly, combination with spina
    bifida, 74, *74*
    contribution to rate of stillbirths, 73
    distribution of, *73*
    environmental factors in, 73
    illustrative example, 81
    incidence of, 73
    recurrence, risk of, 77
    stillbirths and abortions in, *76*
anoxia, in newborn, 221
antibodies, in blood, 137
antigens, in blood, 137
asphyxia, in newborn, 221

271

asthma, hereditary nature of, 132
atomic bomb, death due to, 212
atrial septal defect, and chromosomal variations, 176

"BLACK BABY" MYTH, 156
Blakeslee, A. F., 42
blood, agglutination, 137
   antigens and antibodies in, 137
   cholesterol level, hereditary factors in, 173
      relationship to body constitution, 165
   genetics, 137–146
      counseling problems in, 144
      illustrative examples, 145
   groups, A-B-O system, 137
      effect on likelihood of erythroblastosis in infant, 143
      classification of, 137
      combinations of, incidence of, 148
      in twins, 24, *25*
      incompatibility of, 138
      M-N system, 139
      use of, in establishing paternity, 148
   hemoglobin, abnormalities in, 144
   Rhesus factors, 139
      and erythroblastosis, 139
      genotypes of, 142, *142*
   serum proteins, genetics of, 144
body size, 163–171
   counseling problems and, 169
   effects of eating habits on, 164
   heredity and, 164
   illustrative examples of counseling problems in, 169
   of child, compared to that of parents, 165, *166*
   relationship to blood cholesterol level, 165
   somatotype classification, 166
   Wetzel Grid, 169
   type, as factor in tuberculosis, 113
bomb, atomic, death due to, 212
brachyphalangy, in establishment of paternity, 150

breast cancer, genetic background of, 179
   risk of incidence of, 180
buccal smears, in chromosome studies, 43

CANCER, 178–182
   and chromosomal variations, 46
   counseling problems in, 181
   etiology of, 178
   genes as cause of, 179
   in mouse, genetic factors in, 179
   of breast, genetic background of, 179
      risk of incidence of, 180
   of stomach, genetic background of, 181
   virus theory of, 180
carcinoma. See *cancer.*
carrier. See *heterozygote.*
central nervous system syndrome, 72–82. See also under specific malformations, e.g., *anencephaly.*
centrencephalic electroencephalogram, in studies of convulsive seizures, 187
cholesterol level, of blood, hereditary factors in, 173
   relationship to body constitution, 165
chorea, Huntington's application of laws of genetics to, 16
   frequency of, 7
chromosomes, in Down's syndrome, *frontispiece*, 51
   irradiation and, 46, 214
   number of, variations in, 42–46
   Philadelphia, 47
   sex, variations in, role in etiology of sexual abnormalities, 44
   studies of, 42–48
   translocation, in Down's syndrome, 53
   variations in, and congenital heart disease, 176
      relation to neoplastic disease, 46
      role in mental anomalies, 45
cleft palate, 118–125
   counseling problems in, 122
   etiologic differences from harelip, possibilities of, 120

cleft palate, genetic background, 120
    illustrative example, 125
    incidence of, 118
        in different ethnic groups, 128
        in men and in mice, 119, *119*
    risk of incidence, 122, *122*
    twin studies in, 121, *121*
clubfoot, 126–131
    and consanguinity, 127
    and spina bifida, 126
    genetic background, 126
    heterogeneity of, 129
    illustrative example, 130
    incidence of, 126
        in different ethnic groups, 128
    risk of incidence of, 129
    sex as factor in incidence of, 126
    twin studies in, 127, *127*, 226, 227
color, of skin. See *skin color.*
congenital dislocation, of hip. See *hip.*
congenital hypertrophic pyloric stenosis.
    See *pyloric stenosis.*
congenital malformations of nervous
    system. See *nervous system;* see also
    under specific malformations, e.g.,
    anencephaly.
consanguinity, 34–41
    and clubfoot, 127
    and mental disease, 205
    and mental retardation, 62
    and rare hereditary diseases, 37, *37*
    as test for hereditary disabilities, 35
    counseling problems in, 38
    incidence of, 37
    Muller's concepts of, 36
    risks of hereditary abnormalities in,
        35, 38
    studies in, shortcomings of, 228
convulsive seizures, 183–193
        association with mental deficiency,
            184
        classification of, 187
        counseling problems in, 189
        etiology of, 183
        familial occurrence of, *185*, 186
        family histories in, inadequacy of,
            185
        illustrative examples, 190–193
        incidence of, 184
        risk of incidence of, 189

convulsive seizures, social stigma asso-
        ciated with, 183
    twin studies in, 184, *184, 185*
cousins, first, marriage of, states in which
        legal, 39, *41*
"cures" for genetic diseases, 83–117. See
    also under specific diseases, e.g., *dia-
    betes mellitus.*

DAVENPORT, C. B., 1
depressive psychosis. See *manic-depres-
    sive psychosis.*
diabetes mellitus, 88–94
        abortion in, 91
        as cause of death, 88
        counseling problems in, 91
        frequency of, 88
        genetic background, 89
        genotype for, 92
        illustrative example, 95
        inheritance of, 90
        menarchial age in, 93
        pregnancy in, 91
        risk of occurrence, 91, *91*
        twin studies in, 90, *90*
diaper test, in phenylketonuria, 84
Dice, L. R., 3
Dight, Charles F., 1, 3–5
Dight Institute, founding of, 1
diseases, genetic, "cures" for, 83–117.
    See also under specific diseases, e.g.,
    diabetes mellitus.
dislocation, congenital, of hip. See *hip.*
dominant gene, definition, 17
donor insemination, 66
Down's syndrome, *frontispiece,* 49–58
        and chromosomal variations, 44
        association with congenital heart
            disease, 174
        chromosomes in, 51
            translocation of, 53
        counseling problems in, 53, 55
        detection of, 55
        etiology of, 50
        illustrative examples, 56
        incidence of, 49
            in United States, 52

Down's syndrome, mosaicism in, 55
    relation to leukemia, 46
    reproductive potentials in, 51
    risk of incidence, age factor in, 51,
        51
dwarfism, illustrative example, 170
dysgenic decision, definition, 13
dysplasia, acetabular. See *hip, congenital
    dislocation of.*
dysrhythmias, electroencephalographic,
    187

EATING HABITS, and body build, 164
    of children, 163
ectomorph, 167
electroencephalogram, centrencephalic,
    in studies of convulsive seizures, 187
embryo, effects of thalidomide on, 222
endomorph, 167
environment, as factor in anencephaly,
        73
    in hydrocephaly, 74
    in mental retardation, 63
    in spina bifida, 74
    effects of, twins used in study of, 23
environmental variables, effects on ge-
    netic interpretation, 218–224
epicanthal fold, 158
epilepsy. See *convulsive seizures.*
erythroblastosis, and Rhesus factors, 139
    illustrative example, 145
    incidence of, effect of A-B-O system,
        143
ethnic groups, variations in incidence of
    congenital abnormalities between, 128
eugenic decision, definition, 13
evolution, physician's role in shaping of,
        228
eye fold, 158

FEVER, rheumatic. See *rheumatic fever.*
fibrocystic disease, 86–88
    carriers of, 86

fibrocystic disease, counseling in, 88
    detection of, 87
    etiology of, 86
    genetic background, 87
    illustrative examples, 94
    incidence of, 87
    of pancreas, application of laws of
        genetics to, 19
finger ridge count, in establishment of
    paternity, 151
    smudges, 157
first cousins, marriage of, states in which
    legal, 39, *41*
fraternal twins. See *twins.*

GARDNER'S SYNDROME, genetic back-
    ground of, 179
gastric carcinoma, genetic background
    of, 181
gene, dominant, definition, 17
    recessive, definition, 17
genetic diseases, "cures" for, 83–117. See
    also under specific diseases, e.g., *dia-
    betes mellitus.*
genetics, counseling in, philosophy for,
        10–15
    primary function of, 11
    range of problems in, 6–9
    relation to religious precepts, 13
    laws of, 16–21
Genetics Centers, names, locations, and
    principal counselors of, 2
genitalia, pigmentation of, 158
genotype, of diabetes mellitus, 92
    of Rhesus factors, 142, *142*
German measles. See *rubella.*
gonadal dysgenesis, and chromosome
    number, 43
grand mal seizures. See *convulsive seiz-
    ures.*
guilt, maternal, 11

HAIR, shape and texture of, 158
Hardy-Weinberg law, 30

harelip, 118–125
  counseling problems in, 122
  environmental factors in, 121
  etiologic differences from cleft palate,
    possibilities of, 120
  genetic background, 120
  illustrative example, 125
  incidence of, 118
    in different ethnic groups, 128
    in men and in mice, 119, *119*
  risk of incidence, 122, *122*
  twin studies in, 121, *121*
heart disease, 172–177
    congenital, 173–177
      and chromosomal variations, 176
      association with Down's syn-
        drome, 174
      illustrative example, 177
      incidence of, 173
      multiple cases in one family, 174
      twin studies in, 175
hemoglobin, abnormalities in, 144
hemophilia, 144
heredity clinics, 3
  study of, historical background, 1
heterozygotes, 28–33
  albinism, 29
  definition, 28
  detection of, 32
  frequency of, ratio to affected individ-
    uals, 30, *31*
  of fibrocystic disease, 86
  of phenylketonuria, 85
hip, congenital dislocation of, 102–107
    counseling problems in, 104
    environmental factors in, 105
    etiology of, 102
    genetic background, 103
    illustrative example, 107
    incidence of, 102
      in different ethnic groups, 128
    prophylactic diagnosis of, 104
    risk of incidence of, 106
    sex as factor in incidence of, 104
    twin studies in, 103, *103*
    variations in incidence from right
      to left, 102
homozygote, definition, 28
Hr reaction, 142

Huntington's chorea, application of laws
    of genetics to, 16
  frequency of, 7
hydrocephaly, combination with spina
    bifida, 74, *74*
  distribution of, *73*
  environmental factors in, 74
  illustrative example, 81
  stillbirths and abortions in, *76*
hypercholesteremia, hereditary factors
  in, 173
hypertension, hereditary factors in, 173
hypertrophic pyloric stenosis. See *pyloric
  stenosis.*

IDENTICAL TWINS. See *twins.*
illegitimacy, incidence of, 147
incest. See *consanguinity.*
insemination, donor, 66
institutionalization, of mentally retarded
  child, 64
intersexuality, and chromosome number,
  43
irradiations. See *radiations.*

KLINEFELTER'S SYNDROME, and chromosomal variations, 43, 44

LAWS OF GENETICS, 16–21
Lenz's law, 35
leukemia, and chromosomal variations,
  46
lips, thickness of, 157

MACKLIN, Madge, 20
malaria, and sickle cell anemia, 218
malformations, congenital, of nervous
  system. See *nervous system.*
manic-depressive psychosis, 205–211

manic-depressive psychosis, and consanguinity, 206
familial incidence of, 208
genetic background of, 207, *208*
hereditary basis of, 210
illustrative example, 211
relationship to suicide, 210
twin studies in, 207, *208*
marriage, consanguineous. See *consanguinity.*
maternal guilt, 11
measles, German. See *rubella.*
twin studies in, 226, *227*
menarche, in diabetic girls, 93
Mendel, Gregor, 1
genetic ratios of, 18
laws of genetics developed by, 16–21
mental anomalies, and chromosomal
variations, 45
mental deficiency, association with convulsive seizures, 184
mental diseases. See *schizophrenias* and
manic-depressive psychosis.
mental retardation, 59–71
and consanguinity, 62
counseling problems in, 63
environmental factors in, 63
genetic factors in, 61–63, *61*
illustrative examples, 68–71
in parent, as factor in adoption of
child, 66
in phenylketonuria, 85
in twins, *61*
indications for institutionalization
in, 64
types of, 62
mesomorph, 167
Minnesota Human Genetics League, 5
M-N system, of blood groups, 139
mongolism. See *Down's syndrome.*
mosaicism, in Down's syndrome, 55
mouse, incidence of harelip and cleft
palate in, 119, *119*
mucoviscidosis. See *fibrocystic disease.*
mutations, deleterious, number carried
by average person, 36
due to radiations, 213
myeloid leukemia, chronic, and chromosomal variations, 46

NEOPLASTIC DISEASE. See *cancer.*
nervous system, congenital malformations of, 72–82. See also under specific malformations,
e.g., *anencephaly.*
counseling in, 77
distribution of main types of,
73, *73*
familial nature of, 75, *75, 76*
prediction of, 77
neurofibromatosis, genetic background
of, 179
neuropsychiatric disease. See under specific psychoses, e.g., *schizophrenias.*
newborn, gross malformations of, incidence, 38
nose width, 157

ODORS, body, similarity in twins, 25
ovaries, irradiation of, 215

PALATE, cleft. See *cleft palate.*
pancreas, fibrocystic disease of, application of laws of genetics to, 19
patent ductus arteriosus, association with
rubella, 175
classification of cases, 176
incidence of, 175
relationship to sex, 175
paternity, disputed, 147–154
anthropologic traits and, 150
blood groups and, 148
brachyphalangy in, 150
finger ridge count in, 151
illustrative examples, 151–154
"Percentage Affected Expected" method,
20, *21*
petit mal seizures. See *convulsive seizures.*
phenocopies, 120
phenylketonuria, 84–86
carriers of, 85